Grade 4
Module 5

Eureka Math™
A Story of Units

Special thanks go to the Gordan A. Cain Center and to the Department of Mathematics at Louisiana State University for their support in the development of Eureka Math.

This book may be purchased from the publisher at commoncore.org
10 9 8 7 6 5 4 3 2

ISBN 978-1-63255-030-9

Name _____   Date _____

1. Draw horizontal lines to decompose each rectangle into the number of rows as indicated. Use the model to give the shaded area as both a sum of unit fractions and as a multiplication sentence.

   a. 2 rows

   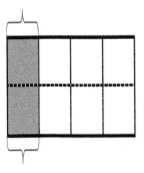

   $$\frac{1}{4} = \frac{2}{}$$

   $$\frac{1}{4} = \frac{1}{8} + \frac{}{} = \frac{}{}$$

   $$\frac{1}{4} = 2 \times \frac{}{} = \frac{}{}$$

   b. 2 rows

   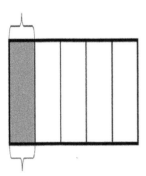

   c. 4 rows

   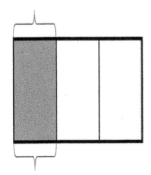

EUREKA MATH™

Lesson 5:   Decompose unit fractions using area models to show equivalence.

2. Draw area models to show the decompositions represented by the number sentences below. Represent the decomposition as a sum of unit fractions and as a multiplication sentence.

a. $\frac{1}{2} = \frac{3}{6}$

b. $\frac{1}{2} = \frac{4}{8}$

c. $\frac{1}{2} = \frac{5}{10}$

d. $\frac{1}{3} = \frac{2}{6}$

e. $\frac{1}{3} = \frac{4}{12}$

f. $\frac{1}{4} = \frac{3}{12}$

3. Explain why $\frac{1}{12} + \frac{1}{12} + \frac{1}{12}$ is the same as $\frac{1}{4}$.

Name _____   Date _____

1. Draw horizontal lines to decompose each rectangle into the number of rows as indicated. Use the model to give the shaded area as both a sum of unit fractions and as a multiplication sentence.

a.   3 rows

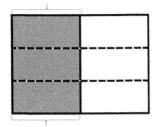

$$\frac{1}{2} = \frac{3}{\rule{1em}{0.4pt}}$$

$$\frac{1}{2} = \frac{1}{6} + \frac{\rule{1em}{0.4pt}}{} + \frac{\rule{1em}{0.4pt}}{} = \frac{3}{6}$$

$$\frac{1}{2} = 3 \times \frac{\rule{1em}{0.4pt}}{} = \frac{3}{6}$$

b.   2 rows

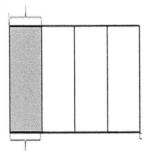

c.   4 rows

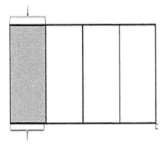

EUREKA
MATH™

Lesson 5:   Decompose unit fractions using area models to show equivalence.

19

2. Draw area models to show the decompositions represented by the number sentences below. Represent the decomposition as a sum of unit fractions and as a multiplication sentence.

a. $\frac{1}{3} = \frac{2}{6}$

b. $\frac{1}{3} = \frac{3}{9}$

c. $\frac{1}{3} = \frac{4}{12}$

d. $\frac{1}{3} = \frac{5}{15}$

e. $\frac{1}{5} = \frac{2}{10}$

f. $\frac{1}{5} = \frac{3}{15}$

3. Explain why $\frac{1}{12} + \frac{1}{12} + \frac{1}{12} + \frac{1}{12}$ is the same as $\frac{1}{3}$.

EUREKA MATH™

Lesson 5: Decompose unit fractions using area models to show equivalence.

Name _____   Date _____

1. Each rectangle represents 1. Draw horizontal lines to decompose each rectangle into the fractional units as indicated. Use the model to give the shaded area as a sum and as a product of unit fractions. Use parentheses to show the relationship between the number sentences. The first one has been partially done for you.

a. Sixths

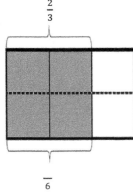

$$\frac{2}{3} = \frac{4}{-}$$

$$\frac{}{3} + \frac{}{3} = \left(\frac{1}{6} + \frac{1}{6}\right) + \left(\frac{1}{6} + \frac{1}{6}\right) = \frac{4}{-}$$

$$\left(\frac{1}{6} + \frac{1}{6}\right) + \left(\frac{1}{6} + \frac{1}{6}\right) = \left(2 \times -\right) + \left(2 \times -\right) = \frac{4}{-}$$

$$\frac{2}{3} = 4 \times - = \frac{4}{-}$$

b. Tenths

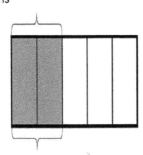

c. Twelfths

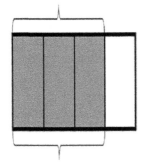

EUREKA
MATH™ | Lesson 6:   Decompose fractions using area models to show equivalence.

21

2. Draw area models to show the decompositions represented by the number sentences below. Express each as a sum and product of unit fractions. Use parentheses to show the relationship between the number sentences.

   a. $\frac{3}{5} = \frac{6}{10}$

   b. $\frac{3}{4} = \frac{6}{8}$

3. Step 1: Draw an area model for a fraction with units of thirds, fourths, or fifths.

   Step 2: Shade in more than one fractional unit.

   Step 3: Partition the area model again to find an equivalent fraction.

   Step 4: Write the equivalent fractions as a number sentence. (If you've written a number sentence like this one already on this Problem Set, start over.)

Name _____   Date _____

1. Each rectangle represents 1. Draw horizontal lines to decompose each rectangle into the fractional units as indicated. Use the model to give the shaded area as a sum and as a product of unit fractions. Use parentheses to show the relationship between the number sentences. The first one has been partially done for you.

a. Tenths

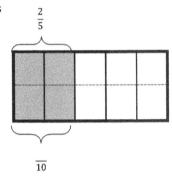

$$\frac{2}{5} = \frac{4}{\ \ }$$

$$\frac{\ }{5} + \frac{\ }{5} = \left(\frac{1}{10} + \frac{1}{10}\right) + \left(\frac{1}{10} + \frac{1}{10}\right) = \frac{4}{\ \ }$$

$$\left(\frac{1}{10} + \frac{1}{10}\right) + \left(\frac{1}{10} + \frac{1}{10}\right) = \left(2 \times \frac{\ }{\ }\right) + \left(2 \times \frac{\ }{\ }\right) = \frac{4}{\ \ }$$

$$\frac{2}{5} = 4 \times \frac{\ }{\ } = \frac{4}{\ \ }$$

b. Eighths

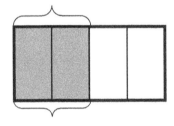

c. Fifteenths

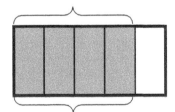

EUREKA
MATH™

2. Draw area models to show the decompositions represented by the number sentences below. Express each as a sum and product of unit fractions. Use parentheses to show the relationship between the number sentences.

a. $\frac{2}{3} = \frac{4}{6}$

b. $\frac{4}{5} = \frac{8}{10}$

3. Step 1: Draw an area model for a fraction with units of thirds, fourths, or fifths.

   Step 2: Shade in more than one fractional unit.

   Step 3: Partition the area model again to find an equivalent fraction.

   Step 4: Write the equivalent fractions as a number sentence. (If you have written a number sentence like this one already in this homework, start over.)

EUREKA
MATH

Lesson 6:   Decompose fractions using area models to show equivalence.

Name _____ Date _____

Each rectangle represents 1.

1. The shaded unit fractions have been decomposed into smaller units. Express the equivalent fractions in a number sentence using multiplication. The first one has been done for you.

a.

$$\frac{1}{2} = \frac{1 \times 2}{2 \times 2} = \frac{2}{4}$$

b.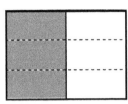

c.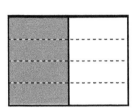

d.

2. Decompose the shaded fractions into smaller units using the area models. Express the equivalent fractions in a number sentence using multiplication.

a.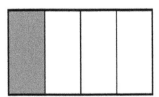

b.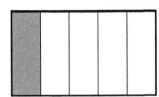

c.

d.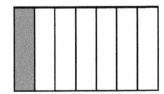

EUREKA MATH

Lesson 7: Use the area model and multiplication to show the equivalence of two fractions.

25

e.   What happened to the size of the fractional units when you decomposed the fraction?

f.   What happened to the total number of units in the whole when you decomposed the fraction?

3.   Draw three different area models to represent 1 third by shading.
     Decompose the shaded fraction into (a) sixths, (b) ninths, and (c) twelfths.
     Use multiplication to show how each fraction is equivalent to 1 third.

     a.

     b.

     c.

Lesson 7:   Use the area model and multiplication to show the equivalence of two
              fractions.

Name _____   Date _____

Each rectangle represents 1.

1. The shaded unit fractions have been decomposed into smaller units. Express the equivalent fractions in a number sentence using multiplication. The first one has been done for you.

a.

$$\frac{1}{2} = \frac{1 \times 2}{2 \times 2} = \frac{2}{4}$$

b.
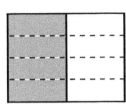

c.
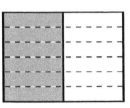

d.
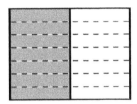

2. Decompose the shaded fractions into smaller units using the area models. Express the equivalent fractions in a number sentence using multiplication.

a.
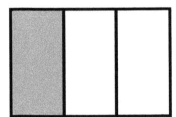

b.
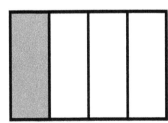

c.

d.
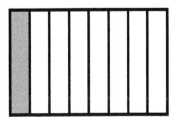

EUREKA MATH™   Lesson 7:   Use the area model and multiplication to show the equivalence of two fractions.

27

3. Draw three different area models to represent 1 fourth by shading.
Decompose the shaded fraction into (a) eighths, (b) twelfths, and (c) sixteenths.
Use multiplication to show how each fraction is equivalent to 1 fourth.

   a.

   b.

   c.

EUREKA
MATH™

Lesson 7:   Use the area model and multiplication to show the equivalence of two
             fractions.

Name _____   Date _____

Each rectangle represents 1.

1. The shaded fractions have been decomposed into smaller units. Express the equivalent fractions in a
    number sentence using multiplication. The first one has been done for you.

a.

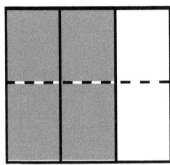

$$\frac{2}{3} = \frac{2 \times 2}{3 \times 2} = \frac{4}{6}$$

b.

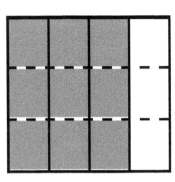

c.

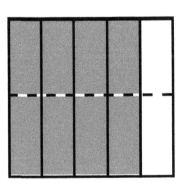

d.

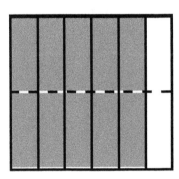

2. Decompose the shaded fractions into smaller units, as given below. Express the equivalent fractions in a
    number sentence using multiplication.

a. Decompose into tenths.

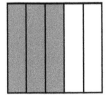

b. Decompose into fifteenths.

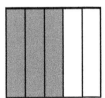

EUREKA MATH   Lesson 8:   Use the area model and multiplication to show the equivalence of two
                                fractions.

29

3. Draw area models to prove that the following number sentences are true.

a. $\frac{2}{5} = \frac{4}{10}$

b. $\frac{2}{3} = \frac{8}{12}$

c. $\frac{3}{6} = \frac{6}{12}$

d. $\frac{4}{6} = \frac{8}{12}$

4. Use multiplication to find an equivalent fraction for each fraction below.

a. $\frac{3}{4}$

b. $\frac{4}{5}$

c. $\frac{7}{6}$

d. $\frac{12}{7}$

5. Determine which of the following are true number sentences. Correct those that are false by changing the right-hand side of the number sentence.

a. $\frac{4}{3} = \frac{8}{9}$

b. $\frac{5}{4} = \frac{10}{8}$

c. $\frac{4}{5} = \frac{12}{10}$

d. $\frac{4}{6} = \frac{12}{18}$

EUREKA MATH

Lesson 8: Use the area model and multiplication to show the equivalence of two fractions.

Name _____   Date _____

Each rectangle represents 1.

1. The shaded fractions have been decomposed into smaller units. Express the equivalent fractions in a
    number sentence using multiplication. The first one has been done for you.

a.

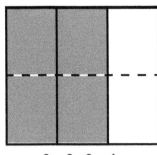

$$\frac{2}{3} = \frac{2 \times 2}{3 \times 2} = \frac{4}{6}$$

b.

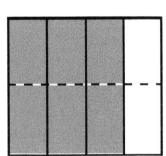

c.

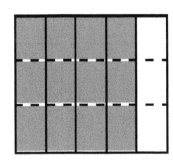

d.

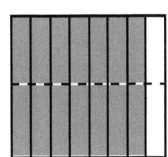

2. Decompose both shaded fractions into twelfths. Express the equivalent fractions in a number sentence
    using multiplication.

a.

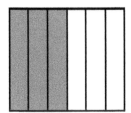

b.

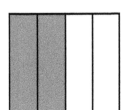

EUREKA MATH

Lesson 8:   Use the area model and multiplication to show the equivalence of two
              fractions.

31

3. Draw area models to prove that the following number sentences are true.

a. $\frac{1}{3} = \frac{2}{6}$

b. $\frac{2}{5} = \frac{4}{10}$

c. $\frac{5}{7} = \frac{10}{14}$

d. $\frac{3}{6} = \frac{9}{18}$

4. Use multiplication to create an equivalent fraction for each fraction below.

a. $\frac{2}{3}$

b. $\frac{5}{6}$

c. $\frac{6}{5}$

d. $\frac{10}{8}$

5. Determine which of the following are true number sentences. Correct those that are false by changing the right-hand side of the number sentence.

a. $\frac{2}{3} = \frac{4}{9}$

b. $\frac{5}{6} = \frac{10}{12}$

c. $\frac{3}{5} = \frac{6}{15}$

d. $\frac{7}{4} = \frac{21}{12}$

EUREKA
MATH™

Lesson 8:   Use the area model and multiplication to show the equivalence of two fractions.

Name _____   Date _____

Each rectangle represents 1.

1. Compose the shaded fractions into larger fractional units. Express the equivalent fractions in a number sentence using division. The first one has been done for you.

a.

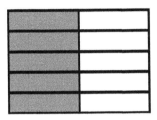

$$\frac{2}{4} = \frac{2 \div 2}{4 \div 2} = \frac{1}{2}$$

b.

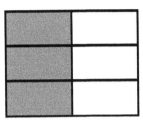

c.

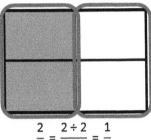

d.

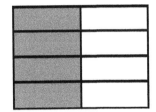

2. Compose the shaded fractions into larger fractional units. Express the equivalent fractions in a number sentence using division.

a.

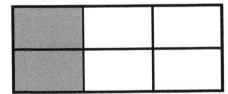

b.

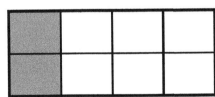

c.

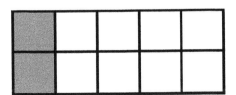

d.

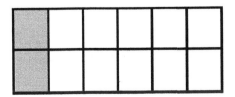

EUREKA MATH™

Lesson 9: Use the area model and division to show the equivalence of two fractions.

33

e.   What happened to the size of the fractional units when you composed the fraction?

f.   What happened to the total number of units in the whole when you composed the fraction?

3.   a.   In the first area model, show 2 sixths. In the second area model, show 3 ninths. Show how both fractions can be renamed as the same unit fraction.

b.   Express the equivalent fractions in a number sentence using division.

4.   a.   In the first area model, show 2 eighths. In the second area model, show 3 twelfths. Show how both fractions can be composed, or renamed, as the same unit fraction.

b.   Express the equivalent fractions in a number sentence using division.

Name _____   Date _____

Each rectangle represents 1.

1. Compose the shaded fractions into larger fractional units. Express the equivalent fractions in a number sentence using division. The first one has been done for you.

a.
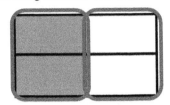

$$\frac{2}{4} = \frac{2 \div 2}{4 \div 2} = \frac{1}{2}$$

b.
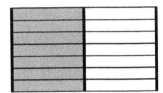

c.
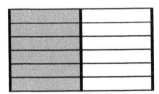

d.
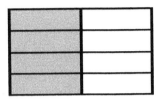

2. Compose the shaded fractions into larger fractional units. Express the equivalent fractions in a number sentence using division.

a.
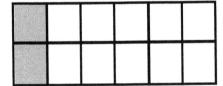

b.
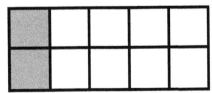

c.
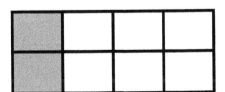

d.
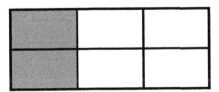

e. What happened to the size of the fractional units when you composed the fraction?

f. What happened to the total number of units in the whole when you composed the fraction?

3. a. In the first area model, show 4 eighths. In the second area model, show 6 twelfths. Show how both fractions can be composed, or renamed, as the same unit fraction.

```
┌──────────────┐    ┌──────────────┐
│              │    │              │
│              │    │              │
│              │    │              │
└──────────────┘    └──────────────┘
```

b. Express the equivalent fractions in a number sentence using division.

4. a. In the first area model, show 4 eighths. In the second area model, show 8 sixteenths. Show how both fractions can be composed, or renamed, as the same unit fraction.

```
┌──────────────┐    ┌──────────────┐
│              │    │              │
│              │    │              │
│              │    │              │
└──────────────┘    └──────────────┘
```

b. Express the equivalent fractions in a number sentence using division.

Name _____   Date _____

Each rectangle represents 1.

1. Compose the shaded fraction into larger fractional units. Express the equivalent fractions in a number sentence using division. The first one has been done for you.

a.

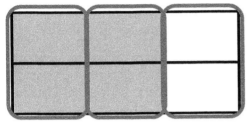

$$\frac{4}{6} = \frac{4 \div 2}{6 \div 2} = \frac{2}{3}$$

b.

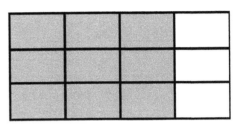

c.

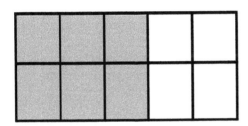

d.

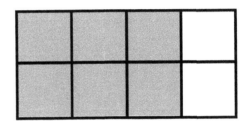

2. Compose the shaded fractions into larger fractional units. Express the equivalent fractions in a number sentence using division.

a.

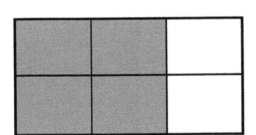

b.

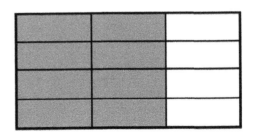

3. Draw an area model to represent each number sentence below.

   a. $\dfrac{4}{10} = \dfrac{4 \div 2}{10 \div 2} = \dfrac{2}{5}$ b. $\dfrac{6}{9} = \dfrac{6 \div 3}{9 \div 3} = \dfrac{2}{3}$

4. Use division to rename each fraction given below. Draw a model if that helps you. See if you can use the largest common factor.

   a. $\dfrac{4}{8}$

   b. $\dfrac{12}{16}$

   c. $\dfrac{12}{20}$

   d. $\dfrac{16}{20}$

Name _____   Date _____

ach rectangle represents 1.

. Compose the shaded fraction into larger fractional units. Express the equivalent fractions in a number sentence using division. The first one has been done for you.

a.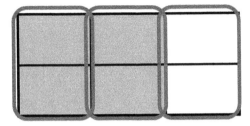

b.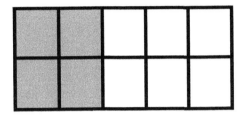

$$\frac{4}{6} = \frac{4 \div 2}{6 \div 2} = \frac{2}{3}$$

c.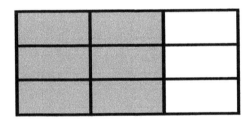

d.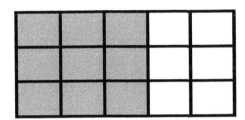

2. Compose the shaded fractions into larger fractional units. Express the equivalent fractions in a number sentence using division.

a.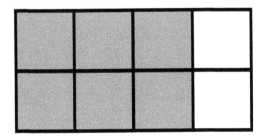

b.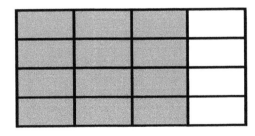

3. Draw an area model to represent each number sentence below.

   a. $\frac{6}{15} = \frac{6 \div 3}{15 \div 3} = \frac{2}{5}$ b. $\frac{6}{18} = \frac{6 \div 3}{18 \div 3} = \frac{2}{6}$

4. Use division to rename each fraction given below. Draw a model if that helps you. See if you can use the largest common factor.

   a. $\frac{8}{10}$

   b. $\frac{9}{12}$

   c. $\frac{8}{12}$

   d. $\frac{12}{18}$

Name _____   Date _____

1. Label each number line with the fractions shown on the tape diagram. Circle the fraction that labels the point on the number line that also names the selected part of the tape diagram.

a.

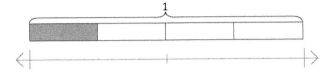

b.

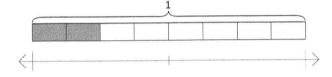

c.

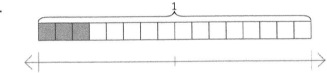

2. Write number sentences using multiplication to show:

a. The fraction represented in 1(a) is equivalent to the fraction represented in 1(b).

b. The fraction represented in 1(a) is equivalent to the fraction represented in 1(c).

EUREKA
MATH™

Lesson 11:   Explain fraction equivalence using a tape diagram and the number line,
and relate that to the use of multiplication and division.

41

3. Use each shaded tape diagram below as a ruler to draw a number line. Mark each number line with the fractional units shown on the tape diagram, and circle the fraction that labels the point on the number line that also names the selected part of the tape diagram.

a.

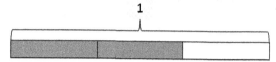

b.

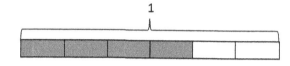

c.

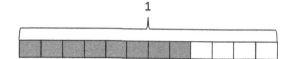

4. Write number sentences using division to show:

    a. The fraction represented in 3(a) is equivalent to the fraction represented in 3(b).

    b. The fraction represented in 3(a) is equivalent to the fraction represented in 3(c).

5. a. Partition a number line from 0 to 1 into fifths. Decompose $\frac{2}{5}$ into 4 equal lengths.

    b. Write a number sentence using multiplication to show what fraction represented on the number line is equivalent to $\frac{2}{5}$.

    c. Write a number sentence using division to show what fraction represented on the number line is equivalent to $\frac{2}{5}$.

EUREKA MATH

Lesson 11:   Explain fraction equivalence using a tape diagram and the number line, and relate that to the use of multiplication and division.

Name _____ Date _____

. Label each number line with the fractions shown on the tape diagram. Circle the fraction that labels the point on the number line that also names the selected part of the tape diagram.

a.

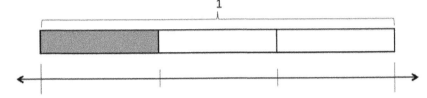

b.

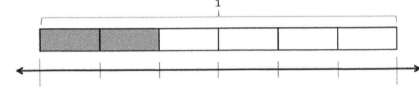

c.

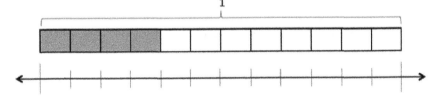

2. Write number sentences using multiplication to show:

a. The fraction represented in 1(a) is equivalent to the fraction represented in 1(b).

b. The fraction represented in 1(a) is equivalent to the fraction represented in 1(c).

EUREKA MATH™

Lesson 11:   Explain fraction equivalence using a tape diagram and the number line, and relate that to the use of multiplication and division.

43

3. Use each shaded tape diagram below as a ruler to draw a number line. Mark each number line with the fractional units shown on the tape diagram, and circle the fraction that labels the point on the number line that also names the selected part of the tape diagram.

a.

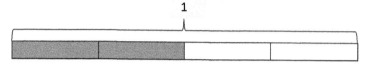

b.

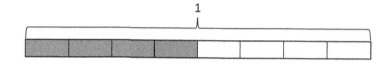

c.

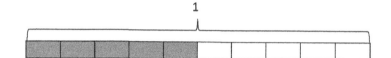

4. Write a number sentence using division to show the fraction represented in 3(a) is equivalent to the fraction represented in 3(b).

5. a. Partition a number line from 0 to 1 into fourths. Decompose $\frac{3}{4}$ into 6 equal lengths.

   b. Write a number sentence using multiplication to show what fraction represented on the number line is equivalent to $\frac{3}{4}$.

   c. Write a number sentence using division to show what fraction represented on the number line is equivalent to $\frac{3}{4}$.

Lesson 11: Explain fraction equivalence using a tape diagram and the number line, and relate that to the use of multiplication and division.

Name _____   Date _____

1.

   a. Plot the following points on the number line without measuring.

       i. $\frac{1}{3}$ ii. $\frac{5}{6}$ iii. $\frac{7}{12}$

   b. Use the number line in Part (a) to compare the fractions by writing >, <, or = on the lines.

       i. $\frac{7}{12}$ _____ $\frac{1}{2}$ ii. $\frac{7}{12}$ _____ $\frac{5}{6}$

2.

   a. Plot the following points on the number line without measuring.

       i. $\frac{11}{12}$ ii. $\frac{1}{4}$ iii. $\frac{3}{8}$

   b. Select two fractions from Part (a), and use the given number line to compare them by writing >, <, or =.

   c. Explain how you plotted the points in Part (a).

EUREKA MATH™   Lesson 12:   Reason using benchmarks to compare two fractions on the number line.

45

3. Compare the fractions given below by writing > or < on the lines.

Give a brief explanation for each answer referring to the benchmarks 0, $\frac{1}{2}$, and 1.

a. $\frac{1}{2}$ _____ $\frac{3}{4}$ b. $\frac{1}{2}$ _____ $\frac{7}{8}$

c. $\frac{2}{3}$ _____ $\frac{2}{5}$ d. $\frac{9}{10}$ _____ $\frac{3}{5}$

e. $\frac{2}{3}$ _____ $\frac{7}{8}$ f. $\frac{1}{3}$ _____ $\frac{2}{4}$

g. $\frac{2}{3}$ _____ $\frac{5}{10}$ h. $\frac{11}{12}$ _____ $\frac{2}{5}$

i. $\frac{49}{100}$ _____ $\frac{51}{100}$ j. $\frac{7}{16}$ _____ $\frac{51}{100}$

Name _____   Date _____

1.

a. Plot the following points on the number line without measuring.

i. $\frac{2}{3}$ ii. $\frac{1}{6}$ iii. $\frac{4}{10}$

0 $\frac{1}{2}$ 1

b. Use the number line in Part (a) to compare the fractions by writing >, <, or = on the lines.

i. $\frac{2}{3}$ _____ $\frac{1}{2}$ ii. $\frac{4}{10}$ _____ $\frac{1}{6}$

2.

a. Plot the following points on the number line without measuring.

i. $\frac{5}{12}$ ii. $\frac{3}{4}$ iii. $\frac{2}{6}$

0 $\frac{1}{2}$ 1

b. Select two fractions from Part (a), and use the given number line to compare them by writing >, <, or =.

c. Explain how you plotted the points in Part (a).

EUREKA
MATH

Lesson 12:   Reason using benchmarks to compare two fractions on the number line.

47

3. Compare the fractions given below by writing > or < on the lines.

   Give a brief explanation for each answer referring to the benchmark of 0, $\frac{1}{2}$, and 1.

a. $\frac{1}{2}$ _____ $\frac{1}{4}$

b. $\frac{6}{8}$ _____ $\frac{1}{2}$

c. $\frac{3}{4}$ _____ $\frac{3}{5}$

d. $\frac{4}{6}$ _____ $\frac{9}{12}$

e. $\frac{2}{3}$ _____ $\frac{1}{4}$

f. $\frac{4}{5}$ _____ $\frac{8}{12}$

g. $\frac{1}{3}$ _____ $\frac{3}{6}$

h. $\frac{7}{8}$ _____ $\frac{3}{5}$

i. $\frac{51}{100}$ _____ $\frac{5}{10}$

j. $\frac{8}{14}$ _____ $\frac{49}{100}$

EUREKA
MATH™

Lesson 12: Reason using benchmarks to compare two fractions on the number line.

Name _____   Date _____

Application Problem:

0                    $\frac{1}{2}$ 1

1.

0                    $\frac{1}{2}$ 1

0                    $\frac{1}{2}$ 1

0                    $\frac{1}{2}$ 1

0                    $\frac{1}{2}$ 1

2.

0                    $\frac{1}{2}$ 1

_____

number line

EUREKA
MATH™

Lesson 12:   Reason using benchmarks to compare two fractions on the number
              line.

49

Name _____   Date _____

1. Place the following fractions on the number line given.

    a. $\dfrac{4}{3}$ b. $\dfrac{11}{6}$ c. $\dfrac{17}{12}$

    1                                    $1\dfrac{1}{2}$ 2

2. Use the number line in Problem 1 to compare the fractions by writing >, <, or = on the lines.

    a. $1\dfrac{5}{6}$ _____ $1\dfrac{5}{12}$ b. $1\dfrac{1}{3}$ _____ $1\dfrac{5}{12}$

3. Place the following fractions on the number line given.

    a. $\dfrac{11}{8}$ b. $\dfrac{7}{4}$ c. $\dfrac{15}{12}$

    1                                    $1\dfrac{1}{2}$ 2

4. Use the number line in Problem 3 to explain the reasoning you used when determining whether $\dfrac{11}{8}$ or $\dfrac{15}{12}$ is greater.

EUREKA
MATH™

Lesson 13:   Reason using benchmarks to compare two fractions on the number line.

51

5. Compare the fractions given below by writing > or < on the lines.
    Give a brief explanation for each answer referring to benchmarks.

a. $\frac{3}{8}$ _____ $\frac{7}{12}$ b. $\frac{5}{12}$ _____ $\frac{7}{8}$

c. $\frac{8}{6}$ _____ $\frac{11}{12}$ d. $\frac{5}{12}$ _____ $\frac{1}{3}$

e. $\frac{7}{5}$ _____ $\frac{11}{10}$ f. $\frac{5}{4}$ _____ $\frac{7}{8}$

g. $\frac{13}{12}$ _____ $\frac{9}{10}$ h. $\frac{6}{8}$ _____ $\frac{5}{4}$

i. $\frac{8}{12}$ _____ $\frac{8}{4}$ j. $\frac{7}{5}$ _____ $\frac{16}{10}$

Name _____   Date _____

1. Place the following fractions on the number line given.

a. $\frac{3}{2}$ b. $\frac{9}{5}$ c. $\frac{14}{10}$

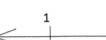

2. Use the number line in Problem 1 to compare the fractions by writing >, <, or = on the lines:

a. $1\frac{1}{6}$ _____ $1\frac{4}{12}$ b. $1\frac{1}{2}$ _____ $1\frac{4}{5}$

3. Place the following fractions on the number line given.

a. $\frac{12}{9}$ b. $\frac{6}{5}$ c. $\frac{18}{15}$

4. Use the number line in Problem 3 to explain the reasoning you used when determining whether $\frac{12}{9}$ or $\frac{18}{15}$ was greater.

EUREKA
MATH™

Lesson 13:   Reason using benchmarks to compare two fractions on the number line.

53

5. Compare the fractions given below by writing > or < on the lines.
   Give a brief explanation for each answer referring to benchmarks.

   a. $\frac{2}{5}$ _____ $\frac{6}{8}$

   b. $\frac{6}{10}$ _____ $\frac{5}{6}$

   c. $\frac{6}{4}$ _____ $\frac{7}{8}$

   d. $\frac{1}{4}$ _____ $\frac{8}{12}$

   e. $\frac{14}{12}$ _____ $\frac{11}{6}$

   f. $\frac{8}{9}$ _____ $\frac{3}{2}$

   g. $\frac{7}{8}$ _____ $\frac{11}{10}$

   h. $\frac{3}{4}$ _____ $\frac{4}{3}$

   i. $\frac{3}{8}$ _____ $\frac{3}{2}$

   j. $\frac{9}{6}$ _____ $\frac{16}{12}$

Name _____   Date _____

blank number lines with midpoint

EUREKA
MATH

Lesson 13:   Reason using benchmarks to compare two fractions on the number line.

55

Name _____   Date _____

1. Compare the pairs of fractions by reasoning about the size of the units. Use >, <, or =.

   a.   1 fourth _____ 1 fifth   b.   3 fourths _____ 3 fifths

   c.   1 tenth _____ 1 twelfth   d.   7 tenths _____ 7 twelfths

2. Compare by reasoning about the following pairs of fractions with the same or related numerators.
   Use >, <, or =. Explain your thinking using words, pictures, or numbers. Problem 2(b) has been done for
   you.

   a. $\frac{3}{5}$ _____ $\frac{3}{4}$

   b. $\frac{2}{5} < \frac{4}{9}$

   because $\frac{2}{5} = \frac{4}{10}$

   4 tenths is less

   than 4 ninths because

   tenths are smaller than ninths.

   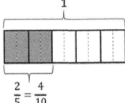

   $\frac{2}{5} = \frac{4}{10}$

   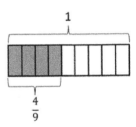

   $\frac{4}{9}$

   c. $\frac{7}{11}$ _____ $\frac{7}{13}$

   d. $\frac{6}{7}$ _____ $\frac{12}{15}$

EUREKA
MATH™   Lesson 14:   Find common units or number of units to compare two fractions.

57

3. Draw two tape diagrams to model each pair of the following fractions with related denominators. Use >, <, or = to compare.

a. $\frac{2}{3}$ _____ $\frac{5}{6}$

b. $\frac{3}{4}$ _____ $\frac{7}{8}$

c. $1\frac{3}{4}$ _____ $1\frac{7}{12}$

4. Draw one number line to model each pair of fractions with related denominators. Use >, <, or = to compare.

a. $\frac{2}{3}$ _____ $\frac{5}{6}$

b. $\frac{3}{8}$ _____ $\frac{1}{4}$

c. $\frac{2}{6}$ _____ $\frac{5}{12}$

d. $\frac{8}{9}$ _____ $\frac{2}{3}$

5. Compare each pair of fractions using >, <, or =. Draw a model if you choose to.

a. $\frac{3}{4}$ _____ $\frac{3}{7}$

b. $\frac{4}{5}$ _____ $\frac{8}{12}$

c. $\frac{7}{10}$ _____ $\frac{3}{5}$

d. $\frac{2}{3}$ _____ $\frac{11}{15}$

e. $\frac{3}{4}$ _____ $\frac{11}{12}$

f. $\frac{7}{3}$ _____ $\frac{7}{4}$

g. $1\frac{1}{3}$ _____ $1\frac{2}{9}$

h. $1\frac{2}{3}$ _____ $1\frac{4}{7}$

6. Timmy drew the picture to the right and claimed that $\frac{2}{3}$ is less than $\frac{7}{12}$. Evan says he thinks $\frac{2}{3}$ is greater than $\frac{7}{12}$. Who is correct? Support your answer with a picture.

EUREKA
MATH™

Lesson 14: Find common units or number of units to compare two fractions.

59

Name _____   Date _____

1. Compare the pairs of fractions by reasoning about the size of the units. Use >, <, or =.

    a.   1 third _____ 1 sixth   b.   2 halves _____ 2 thirds

    c.   2 fourths _____ 2 sixths   d.   5 eighths _____ 5 tenths

2. Compare by reasoning about the following pairs of fractions with the same or related numerators.
    Use >, <, or =. Explain your thinking using words, pictures, or numbers. Problem 2(b) has been done for
    you.

    a. $\frac{3}{6}$ _____ $\frac{3}{7}$

    b. $\frac{2}{5} < \frac{4}{9}$

    because $\frac{2}{5} = \frac{4}{10}$

    4 tenths is less

    than 4 ninths because

    tenths are smaller than ninths.

    c. $\frac{3}{11}$ _____ $\frac{3}{13}$

    d. $\frac{5}{7}$ _____ $\frac{10}{13}$

3. Draw two tape diagrams to model each pair of the following fractions with related denominators.
    Use >, <, or = to compare.

    a. $\frac{3}{4}$ _____ $\frac{7}{12}$

    b. $\frac{2}{4}$ _____ $\frac{1}{8}$

    c. $1\frac{4}{10}$ _____ $1\frac{3}{5}$

4. Draw one number line to model each pair of fractions with related denominators. Use >, <, or = to compare.

a. $\frac{3}{4}$ _____ $\frac{5}{8}$

b. $\frac{11}{12}$ _____ $\frac{3}{4}$

c. $\frac{4}{5}$ _____ $\frac{7}{10}$

d. $\frac{8}{9}$ _____ $\frac{2}{3}$

5. Compare each pair of fractions using >, <, or =. Draw a model if you choose to.

a. $\frac{1}{7}$ _____ $\frac{2}{7}$

b. $\frac{5}{7}$ _____ $\frac{11}{14}$

c. $\frac{7}{10}$ _____ $\frac{3}{5}$

d. $\frac{2}{3}$ _____ $\frac{9}{15}$

e. $\frac{3}{4}$ _____ $\frac{9}{12}$

f. $\frac{5}{3}$ _____ $\frac{5}{2}$

g. $\frac{4}{3}$ _____ $1\frac{2}{9}$

h. $1\frac{1}{3}$ _____ $\frac{9}{7}$

6. Simon claims $\frac{4}{9}$ is greater than $\frac{1}{3}$. Ted thinks $\frac{4}{9}$ is less than $\frac{1}{3}$. Who is correct? Support your answer with a picture.

EUREKA MATH

Lesson 14:   Find common units or number of units to compare two fractions.

61

Name _____   Date _____

1. Draw an area model for each pair of fractions, and use it to compare the two fractions by writing >, <, or =
    on the line. The first two have been partially done for you. Each rectangle represents 1.

a. $\frac{1}{2}$ _____<_____ $\frac{2}{3}$

$$\frac{1\times3}{2\times3} = \frac{3}{6}$$

$$\frac{2\times2}{3\times2} = \frac{4}{6}$$

b. $\frac{4}{5}$ _____ $\frac{3}{4}$

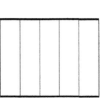

c. $\frac{3}{5}$ _____ $\frac{4}{7}$

d. $\frac{3}{7}$ _____ $\frac{2}{6}$

e. $\frac{5}{8}$ _____ $\frac{6}{9}$

f. $\frac{2}{3}$ _____ $\frac{3}{4}$

EUREKA
MATH™

Lesson 15:   Find common units or number of units to compare two fractions.

63

2. Rename the fractions, as needed, using multiplication in order to compare each pair of fractions by writing >, <, or =.

a. $\dfrac{3}{5}$ _____ $\dfrac{5}{6}$

b. $\dfrac{2}{6}$ _____ $\dfrac{3}{8}$

c. $\dfrac{7}{5}$ _____ $\dfrac{10}{8}$

d. $\dfrac{4}{3}$ _____ $\dfrac{6}{5}$

3. Use any method to compare the fractions. Record your answer using >, <, or =.

a. $\dfrac{3}{4}$ _____ $\dfrac{7}{8}$

b. $\dfrac{6}{8}$ _____ $\dfrac{3}{5}$

c. $\dfrac{6}{4}$ _____ $\dfrac{8}{6}$

d. $\dfrac{8}{5}$ _____ $\dfrac{9}{6}$

4. Explain two ways you have learned to compare fractions. Provide evidence using words, pictures, or numbers.

EUREKA MATH

Lesson 15: Find common units or number of units to compare two fractions.

Name _____   Date _____

1. Draw an area model for each pair of fractions, and use it to compare the two fractions by writing
    >, <, or = on the line. The first two have been partially done for you. Each rectangle represents 1.

a. $\frac{1}{2}$ ____<____ $\frac{3}{5}$

$\frac{1×5}{2×5} = \frac{5}{10}$ $\frac{3×2}{5×2} = \frac{6}{10}$

$\frac{5}{10} < \frac{6}{10}$ so $\frac{1}{2} < \frac{3}{5}$

b. $\frac{2}{3}$ _____ $\frac{3}{4}$

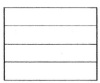

c. $\frac{4}{6}$ _____ $\frac{5}{8}$

d. $\frac{2}{7}$ _____ $\frac{3}{5}$

e. $\frac{4}{6}$ _____ $\frac{6}{9}$

f. $\frac{4}{5}$ _____ $\frac{5}{6}$

EUREKA
MATH™

Lesson 15:   Find common units or number of units to compare two fractions.

65

2. Rename the fractions, as needed, using multiplication in order to compare each pair of fractions by writing >, <, or =.

   a. $\frac{2}{3}$ _____ $\frac{2}{4}$ b. $\frac{4}{7}$ _____ $\frac{1}{2}$

   c. $\frac{5}{4}$ _____ $\frac{9}{8}$ d. $\frac{8}{12}$ _____ $\frac{5}{8}$

3. Use any method to compare the fractions. Record your answer using >, <, or =.

   a. $\frac{8}{9}$ _____ $\frac{2}{3}$ b. $\frac{4}{7}$ _____ $\frac{4}{5}$

   c. $\frac{3}{2}$ _____ $\frac{9}{6}$ d. $\frac{11}{7}$ _____ $\frac{5}{3}$

4. Explain which method you prefer using to compare fractions. Provide an example using words, pictures, or numbers.

Name _____   Date _____

1. Solve.

   a.   3 fifths – 1 fifth = _____   b.   5 fifths – 3 fifths = _____

   c.   3 halves – 2 halves = _____   d.   6 fourths – 3 fourths = _____

2. Solve.

   a. $\dfrac{5}{6} - \dfrac{3}{6}$ b. $\dfrac{6}{8} - \dfrac{4}{8}$

   c. $\dfrac{3}{10} - \dfrac{3}{10}$ d. $\dfrac{5}{5} - \dfrac{4}{5}$

   e. $\dfrac{5}{4} - \dfrac{4}{4}$ f. $\dfrac{5}{4} - \dfrac{3}{4}$

3. Solve. Use a number bond to show how to convert the difference to a mixed number. Problem (a) has been completed for you.

   a. $\dfrac{12}{8} - \dfrac{3}{8} = \dfrac{9}{8} \quad = 1\dfrac{1}{8}$ b. $\dfrac{12}{6} - \dfrac{5}{6}$

   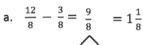

   c. $\dfrac{9}{5} - \dfrac{3}{5}$ d. $\dfrac{14}{8} - \dfrac{3}{8}$

   e. $\dfrac{8}{4} - \dfrac{2}{4}$ f. $\dfrac{15}{10} - \dfrac{3}{10}$

EUREKA MATH™   Lesson 16:   Use visual models to add and subtract two fractions with the same units.

67

4. Solve. Write the sum in unit form.

   a. 2 fourths + 1 fourth = _____   b. 4 fifths + 3 fifths = _____

5. Solve.

   a. $\frac{2}{8} + \frac{5}{8}$ b. $\frac{4}{12} + \frac{5}{12}$

6. Solve. Use a number bond to decompose the sum. Record your final answer as a mixed number. Problem (a) has been completed for you.

   a. $\frac{3}{5} + \frac{4}{5} = \frac{7}{5} = 1\frac{2}{5}$

   $\frac{5}{5}$ $\frac{2}{5}$

   b. $\frac{4}{4} + \frac{3}{4}$

   c. $\frac{6}{9} + \frac{6}{9}$ d. $\frac{7}{10} + \frac{6}{10}$

   e. $\frac{5}{6} + \frac{7}{6}$ f. $\frac{9}{8} + \frac{5}{8}$

7. Solve. Use a number line to model your answer.

   a. $\frac{7}{4} - \frac{5}{4}$

   b. $\frac{5}{4} + \frac{2}{4}$

Name _____   Date _____

1. Solve.

   a. 3 sixths – 2 sixths = _____   b. 5 tenths – 3 tenths = _____

   c. 3 fourths – 2 fourths = _____   d. 5 thirds – 2 thirds = _____

2. Solve.

   a. $\frac{3}{5} - \frac{2}{5}$ b. $\frac{7}{9} - \frac{3}{9}$

   c. $\frac{7}{12} - \frac{3}{12}$ d. $\frac{6}{6} - \frac{4}{6}$

   e. $\frac{5}{3} - \frac{2}{3}$ f. $\frac{7}{4} - \frac{5}{4}$

3. Solve. Use a number bond to decompose the difference. Record your final answer as a mixed number.
   Problem (a) has been completed for you.

   a. $\frac{12}{6} - \frac{3}{6} = \frac{9}{6} = 1\frac{3}{6}$ b. $\frac{17}{8} - \frac{6}{8}$

   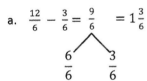

   c. $\frac{9}{5} - \frac{3}{5}$ d. $\frac{11}{4} - \frac{6}{4}$

   e. $\frac{10}{7} - \frac{2}{7}$ f. $\frac{21}{10} - \frac{9}{10}$

EUREKA
MATH™ | Lesson 16:   Use visual models to add and subtract two fractions with the same
                                       units.

4. Solve. Write the sum in unit form.

    a. 4 fifths + 2 fifths = _____   b. 5 eighths + 2 eighths = _____

5. Solve.

    a. $\frac{3}{11} + \frac{6}{11}$ b. $\frac{3}{10} + \frac{6}{10}$

6. Solve. Use a number bond to decompose the sum. Record your final answer as a mixed number.

    a. $\frac{3}{4} + \frac{3}{4}$ b. $\frac{8}{12} + \frac{6}{12}$

    c. $\frac{5}{8} + \frac{7}{8}$ d. $\frac{8}{10} + \frac{5}{10}$

    e. $\frac{3}{5} + \frac{6}{5}$ f. $\frac{4}{3} + \frac{2}{3}$

7. Solve. Use a number line to model your answer.

    a. $\frac{11}{9} - \frac{5}{9}$

    b. $\frac{13}{12} + \frac{4}{12}$

Name _____   Date _____

<-->

<-->

<-->

<-->

<-->

<-->

blank number lines

Lesson 16:   Use visual models to add and subtract two fractions with the same
             units.

71

Name _____   Date _____

. Use the following three fractions to write two subtraction and two addition number sentences.

a. $\dfrac{8}{5}, \dfrac{2}{5}, \dfrac{10}{5}$	b. $\dfrac{15}{8}, \dfrac{7}{8}, \dfrac{8}{8}$

. Solve. Model each subtraction problem with a number line, and solve by both counting up and subtracting. Part (a) has been completed for you.

a. $1 - \dfrac{3}{4}$

$\dfrac{4}{4} - \dfrac{3}{4} = \dfrac{1}{4}$

b. $1 - \dfrac{8}{10}$

c. $1 - \dfrac{3}{5}$

d. $1 - \dfrac{5}{8}$

e. $1\dfrac{2}{10} - \dfrac{7}{10}$

f. $1\dfrac{1}{5} - \dfrac{3}{5}$

EUREKA
MATH

Lesson 17:   Use visual models to add and subtract two fractions with the same units, including subtracting from one whole.

73

3. Find the difference in two ways. Use number bonds to decompose the total. Part (a) has been completed for you.

a. $1\frac{2}{5} - \frac{4}{5}$

$\frac{5}{5} + \frac{2}{5} = \frac{7}{5}$

$\frac{7}{5} - \frac{4}{5} = \boxed{\frac{3}{5}}$

$\frac{5}{5} - \frac{4}{5} = \frac{1}{5}$

$\frac{1}{5} + \frac{2}{5} = \boxed{\frac{3}{5}}$

b. $1\frac{3}{6} - \frac{4}{6}$

c. $1\frac{6}{8} - \frac{7}{8}$

d. $1\frac{1}{10} - \frac{7}{10}$

e. $1\frac{3}{12} - \frac{6}{12}$

Name _____   Date _____

1. Use the following three fractions to write two subtraction and two addition number sentences.

a. $\frac{5}{6}, \frac{4}{6}, \frac{9}{6}$	b. $\frac{5}{9}, \frac{13}{9}, \frac{8}{9}$

2. Solve. Model each subtraction problem with a number line, and solve by both counting up and subtracting.

a. $1 - \frac{5}{8}$ b. $1 - \frac{2}{5}$

c. $1\frac{3}{6} - \frac{5}{6}$ d. $1 - \frac{1}{4}$

e. $1\frac{1}{3} - \frac{2}{3}$ f. $1\frac{1}{5} - \frac{2}{5}$

EUREKA MATH™   Lesson 17: Use visual models to add and subtract two fractions with the same units, including subtracting from one whole.

75

3. Find the difference in two ways. Use number bonds to decompose the total. Part (a) has been completed for you.

a. $1\frac{2}{5} - \frac{4}{5}$

$\frac{5}{5}$ $\frac{2}{5}$

$\frac{5}{5} + \frac{2}{5} = \frac{7}{5}$

$\frac{7}{5} - \frac{4}{5} = \frac{3}{5}$

$\frac{5}{5} - \frac{4}{5} = \frac{1}{5}$

$\frac{1}{5} + \frac{2}{5} = \frac{3}{5}$

b. $1\frac{3}{8} - \frac{7}{8}$

c. $1\frac{1}{4} - \frac{3}{4}$

d. $1\frac{2}{7} - \frac{5}{7}$

e. $1\frac{3}{10} - \frac{7}{10}$

Lesson 17:   Use visual models to add and subtract two fractions with the same units, including subtracting from one whole.

Name _____ Date _____

1. Show one way to solve each problem. Express sums and differences as a mixed number when possible. Use number bonds when it helps you. Part (a) is partially completed.

a. $\frac{2}{5} + \frac{3}{5} + \frac{1}{5}$ $= \frac{5}{5} + \frac{1}{5} = 1 + \frac{1}{5}$ $= $ _____	b. $\frac{3}{6} + \frac{1}{6} + \frac{3}{6}$	c. $\frac{5}{7} + \frac{7}{7} + \frac{2}{7}$
d. $\frac{7}{8} - \frac{3}{8} - \frac{1}{8}$	e. $\frac{7}{9} + \frac{1}{9} + \frac{4}{9}$	f. $\frac{4}{10} + \frac{11}{10} + \frac{5}{10}$
g. $1 - \frac{3}{12} - \frac{4}{12}$	h. $1\frac{2}{3} - \frac{1}{3} - \frac{1}{3}$	i. $\frac{10}{12} + \frac{5}{12} + \frac{2}{12} + \frac{7}{12}$

2. Monica and Stuart used different strategies to solve $\frac{5}{8} + \frac{2}{8} + \frac{5}{8}$.

| **Monica's Way** | **Stuart's Way** |

$$\frac{5}{8} + \frac{2}{8} + \frac{5}{8} = \frac{7}{8} + \frac{5}{8} = \frac{8}{8} + \frac{4}{8} = 1\frac{4}{8}$$

$$\frac{1}{8} \quad \frac{4}{8}$$

$$\frac{5}{8} + \frac{2}{8} + \frac{5}{8} = \frac{12}{8} = 1 + \frac{4}{8} = 1\frac{4}{8}$$

$$\frac{8}{8} \quad \frac{4}{8}$$

Whose strategy do you like best? Why?

3. You gave one solution for each part of Problem 1. Now, for each problem indicated below, give a different solution method.

1(c) $\frac{5}{7} + \frac{7}{7} + \frac{2}{7}$

1(f) $\frac{4}{10} + \frac{11}{10} + \frac{5}{10}$

1(g) $1 - \frac{3}{12} - \frac{4}{12}$

Name _____   Date _____

1. Show one way to solve each problem. Express sums and differences as a mixed number when possible. Use number bonds when it helps you. Part (a) is partially completed.

a. $\frac{1}{3} + \frac{2}{3} + \frac{1}{3}$ $= \frac{3}{3} + \frac{1}{3} = 1 + \frac{1}{3}$ $=$ _____	b. $\frac{5}{8} + \frac{5}{8} + \frac{3}{8}$	c. $\frac{4}{6} + \frac{6}{6} + \frac{1}{6}$
d. $1\frac{2}{12} - \frac{2}{12} - \frac{1}{12}$	e. $\frac{5}{7} + \frac{1}{7} + \frac{4}{7}$	f. $\frac{4}{10} + \frac{7}{10} + \frac{9}{10}$
g. $1 - \frac{3}{10} - \frac{1}{10}$	h. $1\frac{3}{5} - \frac{4}{5} - \frac{1}{5}$	i. $\frac{10}{15} + \frac{7}{15} + \frac{12}{15} + \frac{1}{15}$

EUREKA MATH   **Lesson 18:**   Add and subtract more than two fractions.

79

2. Bonnie used two different strategies to solve $\frac{5}{10} + \frac{4}{10} + \frac{3}{10}$.

Bonnie's First Strategy   **Bonnie's Second Strategy**

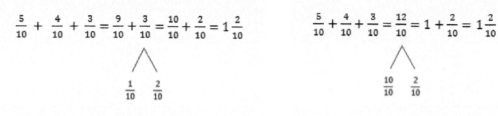

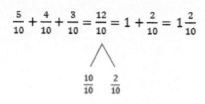

Which strategy do you like best? Why?

3. You gave one solution for each part of Problem 1. Now, for each problem indicated below, give a different solution method.

   1(b) $\frac{5}{8} + \frac{5}{8} + \frac{3}{8}$

   1(e) $\frac{5}{7} + \frac{1}{7} + \frac{4}{7}$

   1(h) $1\frac{3}{5} - \frac{4}{5} - \frac{1}{5}$

Name _____ Date _____

Use the RDW process to solve.

1. Sue ran $\frac{9}{10}$ mile on Monday and $\frac{7}{10}$ mile on Tuesday. How many miles did Sue run in the 2 days?

2. Mr. Salazar cut his son's birthday cake into 8 equal pieces. Mr. Salazar, Mrs. Salazar, and the birthday boy each ate 1 piece of cake. What fraction of the cake was left?

3. Maria spent $\frac{4}{7}$ of her money on a book and saved the rest. What fraction of her money did Maria save?

Lesson 19:   Solve word problems involving addition and subtraction of fractions.

81

4. Mrs. Jones had $1\frac{4}{8}$ pizzas left after a party. After giving some to Gary, she had $\frac{7}{8}$ pizza left. What fraction of a pizza did she give Gary?

5. A baker had 2 pans of corn bread. He served $1\frac{1}{4}$ pans. What fraction of a pan was left?

6. Marius combined $\frac{4}{8}$ gallon of lemonade, $\frac{3}{8}$ gallon of cranberry juice, and $\frac{6}{8}$ gallon of soda water to make punch for a party. How many gallons of punch did he make in all?

EUREKA
MATH™

Lesson 19:   Solve word problems involving addition and subtraction of fractions.

Name _____   Date _____

Use the RDW process to solve.

1. Isla walked $\frac{3}{4}$ mile each way to and from school on Wednesday. How many miles did Isla walk that day?

2. Zach spent $\frac{2}{3}$ hour reading on Friday and $1\frac{1}{3}$ hours reading on Saturday. How much more time did he read on Saturday than on Friday?

3. Mrs. Cashmore bought a large melon. She cut a piece that weighed $1\frac{1}{8}$ pounds and gave it to her neighbor. The remaining piece of melon weighed $\frac{6}{8}$ pound. How much did the whole melon weigh?

EUREKA MATH™   Lesson 19:   Solve word problems involving addition and subtraction of fractions.

83

4. Ally's little sister wanted to help her make some oatmeal cookies. First, she put $\frac{5}{8}$ cup of oatmeal in the bowl. Next, she added another $\frac{5}{8}$ cup of oatmeal. Finally, she added another $\frac{5}{8}$ cup of oatmeal. How much oatmeal did she put in the bowl?

5. Marcia baked 2 pans of brownies. Her family ate $1\frac{5}{6}$ pans. What fraction of a pan of brownies was left?

6. Joanie wrote a letter that was $1\frac{1}{4}$ pages long. Katie wrote a letter that was $\frac{3}{4}$ page shorter than Joanie's letter. How long was Katie's letter?

Name _____   Date _____

1. Use a tape diagram to represent each addend. Decompose one of the tape diagrams to make like units. Then, write the complete number sentence. Part (a) is partially completed.

a. $\frac{1}{4} + \frac{1}{8}$

b. $\frac{1}{4} + \frac{1}{12}$

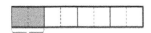

$$\frac{}{8} + \frac{}{8} = \frac{}{8}$$

c. $\frac{2}{6} + \frac{1}{3}$

d. $\frac{1}{2} + \frac{3}{8}$

e. $\frac{3}{10} + \frac{3}{5}$

f. $\frac{2}{3} + \frac{2}{9}$

EUREKA
MATH™

Lesson 20:   Use visual models to add two fractions with related units using the
              denominators 2, 3, 4, 5, 6, 8, 10, and 12.

85

2. Estimate to determine if the sum is between 0 and 1 or 1 and 2. Draw a number line to model the addition. Then, write a complete number sentence. Part (a) has been completed for you.

a. $\frac{1}{2} + \frac{1}{4}$ $\frac{2}{4} + \frac{1}{4} = \frac{3}{4}$

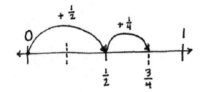

b. $\frac{1}{2} + \frac{4}{10}$

c. $\frac{6}{10} + \frac{1}{2}$

d. $\frac{2}{3} + \frac{3}{6}$

e. $\frac{3}{4} + \frac{6}{8}$

f. $\frac{4}{10} + \frac{6}{5}$

3. Solve the following addition problem without drawing a model. Show your work.

$$\frac{2}{3} + \frac{4}{6}$$

EUREKA
MATH™

Lesson 20:   Use visual models to add two fractions with related units using the denominators 2, 3, 4, 5, 6, 8, 10, and 12.

Name _____ Date _____

Use a tape diagram to represent each addend. Decompose one of the tape diagrams to make like units. Then, write the complete number sentence.

a. $\frac{1}{3} + \frac{1}{6}$

b. $\frac{1}{2} + \frac{1}{4}$

c. $\frac{3}{4} + \frac{1}{8}$

d. $\frac{1}{4} + \frac{5}{12}$

e. $\frac{3}{8} + \frac{1}{2}$

f. $\frac{3}{5} + \frac{3}{10}$

EUREKA MATH

Lesson 20: Use visual models to add two fractions with related units using the denominators 2, 3, 4, 5, 6, 8, 10, and 12.

87

2. Estimate to determine if the sum is between 0 and 1 or 1 and 2. Draw a number line to model the addition. Then, write a complete number sentence. The first one has been completed for you.

a. $\frac{1}{3} + \frac{1}{6}$ $\frac{2}{6} + \frac{1}{6} = \frac{3}{6}$

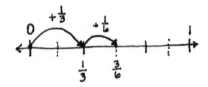

b. $\frac{3}{5} + \frac{7}{10}$

c. $\frac{5}{12} + \frac{1}{4}$

d. $\frac{3}{4} + \frac{5}{8}$

e. $\frac{7}{8} + \frac{3}{4}$

f. $\frac{1}{6} + \frac{5}{3}$

3. Solve the following addition problem without drawing a model. Show your work.

$$\frac{5}{6} + \frac{1}{3}$$

Lesson 20: Use visual models to add two fractions with related units using the denominators 2, 3, 4, 5, 6, 8, 10, and 12.

Name _____   Date _____

1. Draw a tape diagram to represent each addend. Decompose one of the tape diagrams to make like units. Then, write a complete number sentence. Use a number bond to write each sum as a mixed number.

    a. $\frac{3}{4} + \frac{1}{2}$ b. $\frac{2}{3} + \frac{3}{6}$

    c. $\frac{5}{6} + \frac{1}{3}$ d. $\frac{4}{5} + \frac{7}{10}$

2. Draw a number line to model the addition. Then, write a complete number sentence. Use a number bond to write each sum as a mixed number.

    a. $\frac{1}{2} + \frac{3}{4}$ b. $\frac{1}{2} + \frac{6}{8}$

EUREKA MATH™ | Lesson 21:   Use visual models to add two fractions with related units using the denominators 2, 3, 4, 5, 6, 8, 10, and 12.

89

c. $\frac{7}{10} + \frac{3}{5}$

d. $\frac{2}{3} + \frac{5}{6}$

3. Solve. Write the sum as a mixed number. Draw a model if needed.

a. $\frac{3}{4} + \frac{2}{8}$

b. $\frac{4}{6} + \frac{1}{2}$

c. $\frac{4}{6} + \frac{2}{3}$

d. $\frac{8}{10} + \frac{3}{5}$

e. $\frac{5}{8} + \frac{3}{4}$

f. $\frac{5}{8} + \frac{2}{4}$

g. $\frac{1}{2} + \frac{5}{8}$

h. $\frac{3}{10} + \frac{4}{5}$

Name _____   Date _____

1. Draw a tape diagram to represent each addend. Decompose one of the tape diagrams to make like units. Then, write a complete number sentence. Use a number bond to write each sum as a mixed number.

a. $\frac{7}{8} + \frac{1}{4}$

b. $\frac{4}{8} + \frac{2}{4}$

c. $\frac{4}{6} + \frac{1}{2}$

d. $\frac{3}{5} + \frac{8}{10}$

2. Draw a number line to model the addition. Then, write a complete number sentence. Use a number bond to write each sum as a mixed number.

a. $\frac{1}{2} + \frac{5}{8}$

b. $\frac{3}{4} + \frac{3}{8}$

EUREKA
MATH

Lesson 21:   Use visual models to add two fractions with related units using the
              denominators 2, 3, 4, 5, 6, 8, 10, and 12.

91

c. $\frac{4}{10} + \frac{4}{5}$

d. $\frac{1}{3} + \frac{5}{6}$

3. Solve. Write the sum as a mixed number. Draw a model if needed.

a. $\frac{1}{2} + \frac{6}{8}$

b. $\frac{7}{8} + \frac{3}{4}$

c. $\frac{5}{6} + \frac{1}{3}$

d. $\frac{9}{10} + \frac{2}{5}$

e. $\frac{4}{12} + \frac{3}{4}$

f. $\frac{1}{2} + \frac{5}{6}$

g. $\frac{3}{12} + \frac{5}{6}$

h. $\frac{7}{10} + \frac{4}{5}$

Name _____   Date _____

. Draw a tape diagram to match each number sentence. Then, complete the number sentence.

a. $3 + \frac{1}{3} =$ _____

b. $4 + \frac{3}{4} =$ _____

c. $3 - \frac{1}{4} =$ _____

d. $5 - \frac{2}{5} =$ _____

2. Use the following three numbers to write two subtraction and two addition number sentences.

a. $6, 6\frac{3}{8}, \frac{3}{8}$

b. $\frac{4}{7}, 9, 8\frac{3}{7}$

3. Solve using a number bond. Draw a number line to represent each number sentence. The first one has been done for you.

a. $4 - \frac{1}{3} =$ $3\frac{2}{3}$

b. $5 - \frac{2}{3} =$ _____

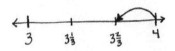

EUREKA
MATH™

Lesson 22:   Add a fraction less than 1 to, or subtract a fraction less than 1 from,
a whole number using decomposition and visual models.

93

c. $7 - \frac{3}{8} =$ _____

d. $10 - \frac{4}{10} =$ _____

4. Complete the subtraction sentences using number bonds.

a. $3 - \frac{1}{10} =$ _____

b. $5 - \frac{3}{4} =$ _____

c. $6 - \frac{5}{8} =$ _____

d. $7 - \frac{3}{9} =$ _____

e. $8 - \frac{6}{10} =$ _____

f. $29 - \frac{9}{12} =$ _____

EUREKA MATH™

Lesson 22:   Add a fraction less than 1 to, or subtract a fraction less than 1 from, a whole number using decomposition and visual models.

Name _____   Date _____

1. Draw a tape diagram to match each number sentence. Then, complete the number sentence.

    a. $2 + \frac{1}{4} =$ _____

    b. $3 + \frac{2}{3} =$ _____

    c. $2 - \frac{1}{5} =$ _____

    d. $3 - \frac{3}{4} =$ _____

2. Use the following three numbers to write two subtraction and two addition number sentences.

    a. $4,\ 4\frac{5}{8}, \frac{5}{8}$

    b. $\frac{2}{7},\ 5\frac{5}{7},\ 6$

3. Solve using a number bond. Draw a number line to represent each number sentence. The first one has been done for you.

    a. $4 - \frac{1}{3} = \quad 3\frac{2}{3}$

    b. $8 - \frac{5}{6} =$ _____

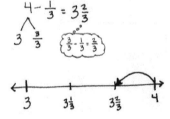

Lesson 22:   Add a fraction less than 1 to, or subtract a fraction less than 1 from, a whole number using decomposition and visual models.

EUREKA
MATH

95

c. $7 - \frac{4}{5} =$ _____

d. $3 - \frac{3}{10} =$ _____

4. Complete the subtraction sentences using number bonds.

a. $6 - \frac{1}{4} =$ _____

b. $7 - \frac{2}{10} =$ _____

c. $5 - \frac{5}{6} =$ _____

d. $6 - \frac{6}{8} =$ _____

e. $3 - \frac{7}{8} =$ _____

f. $26 - \frac{7}{10} =$ _____

EUREKA
MATH

Lesson 22:   Add a fraction less than 1 to, or subtract a fraction less than 1 from,
a whole number using decomposition and visual models.

Name _____   Date _____

1. Circle any fractions that are equivalent to a whole number. Record the whole number below the fraction.

   a. Count by 1 thirds. Start at 0 thirds. End at 6 thirds.

   $\dfrac{0}{3},\ \dfrac{1}{3},$

   0

   b. Count by 1 halves. Start at 0 halves. End at 8 halves.

2. Use parentheses to show how to make ones in the following number sentence.

   $$\frac{1}{4}+\frac{1}{4}+\frac{1}{4}+\frac{1}{4}+\ \frac{1}{4}+\frac{1}{4}+\frac{1}{4}+\frac{1}{4}+\ \frac{1}{4}+\frac{1}{4}+\frac{1}{4}+\frac{1}{4}=3$$

3. Multiply, as shown below. Draw a number line to support your answer.

   a. $6 \times \dfrac{1}{3}$

   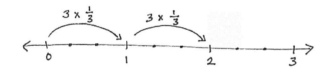

   $$6 \times \frac{1}{3} = 2 \times \frac{3}{3} = 2$$

   b. $6 \times \dfrac{1}{2}$

   c. $12 \times \dfrac{1}{4}$

EUREKA MATH™

Lesson 23:   Add and multiply unit fractions to build fractions greater than 1 using visual models.

97

4. Multiply, as shown below. Write the product as a mixed number. Draw a number line to support your answer.

    a.   7 copies of 1 third

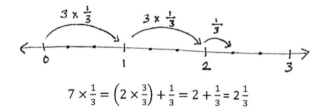

$$7 \times \frac{1}{3} = \left(2 \times \frac{3}{3}\right) + \frac{1}{3} = 2 + \frac{1}{3} = 2\frac{1}{3}$$

    b.   7 copies of 1 half

    c. $10 \times \frac{1}{4}$

    d. $14 \times \frac{1}{3}$

EUREKA
MATH

Lesson 23:   Add and multiply unit fractions to build fractions greater than 1 using
              visual models.

Name _____   Date _____

. Circle any fractions that are equivalent to a whole number. Record the whole number below the fraction.

a. Count by 1 fourths. Start at 0 fourths. Stop at 6 fourths.

$\dfrac{0}{4}, \dfrac{1}{4},$

0

b. Count by 1 sixths. Start at 0 sixths. Stop at 14 sixths.

2. Use parentheses to show how to make ones in the following number sentence.

$$\frac{1}{3}+\frac{1}{3}+\frac{1}{3}+\frac{1}{3}+\frac{1}{3}+\frac{1}{3}+\frac{1}{3}+\frac{1}{3}+\frac{1}{3}+\frac{1}{3}+\frac{1}{3}+\frac{1}{3}=4$$

3. Multiply, as shown below. Draw a number line to support your answer.

a. $6 \times \dfrac{1}{3}$

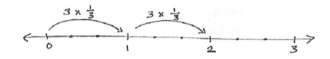

$$6 \times \frac{1}{3} = 2 \times \frac{3}{3} = 2$$

b. $10 \times \dfrac{1}{2}$

c. $8 \times \dfrac{1}{4}$

EUREKA
MATH

Lesson 23:   Add and multiply unit fractions to build fractions greater than 1 using
visual models.

99

4. Multiply, as shown below. Write the product as a mixed number. Draw a number line to support your answer.

a. 7 copies of 1 third

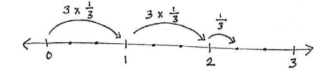

$$7 \times \frac{1}{3} = \left(2 \times \frac{3}{3}\right) + \frac{1}{3} = 2 + \frac{1}{3} = 2\frac{1}{3}$$

b. 7 copies of 1 fourth

c. 11 groups of 1 fifth

d. $7 \times \frac{1}{2}$

e. $9 \times \frac{1}{5}$

EUREKA
MATH

Lesson 23:   Add and multiply unit fractions to build fractions greater than 1 using visual models.

Name _____   Date _____

. Rename each fraction as a mixed number by decomposing it into two parts as shown below. Model the decomposition with a number line and a number bond.

a. $\frac{11}{3}$

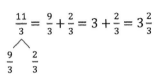

$$\frac{11}{3} = \frac{9}{3} + \frac{2}{3} = 3 + \frac{2}{3} = 3\frac{2}{3}$$

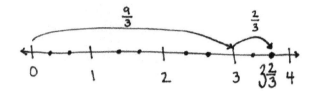

b. $\frac{12}{5}$

c. $\frac{13}{2}$

d. $\frac{15}{4}$

EUREKA
MATH

Lesson 24:   Decompose and compose fractions greater than 1 to express them in
             various forms.

101

2. Convert each fraction to a mixed number. Show your work as in the example. Model with a number line.

a. $\dfrac{11}{3}$

   $$\dfrac{11}{3} = \dfrac{3 \times 3}{3} + \dfrac{2}{3} = 3 + \dfrac{2}{3} = 3\dfrac{2}{3}$$

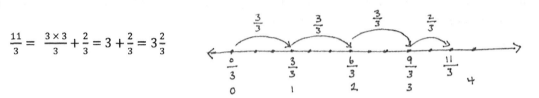

b. $\dfrac{9}{2}$

c. $\dfrac{17}{4}$

3. Convert each fraction to a mixed number.

a. $\dfrac{9}{4} =$	b. $\dfrac{17}{5} =$	c. $\dfrac{25}{6} =$
d. $\dfrac{30}{7} =$	e. $\dfrac{38}{8} =$	f. $\dfrac{48}{9} =$
g. $\dfrac{63}{10} =$	h. $\dfrac{84}{10} =$	i. $\dfrac{37}{12} =$

Name _____ Date _____

. Rename each fraction as a mixed number by decomposing it into two parts as shown below. Model the decomposition with a number line and a number bond.

a. $\frac{11}{3}$

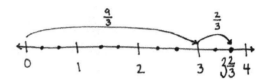

$$\frac{11}{3} = \frac{9}{3} + \frac{2}{3} = 3 + \frac{2}{3} = 3\frac{2}{3}$$

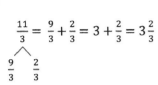

b. $\frac{13}{4}$

c. $\frac{16}{5}$

d. $\frac{15}{2}$

e. $\frac{17}{3}$

EUREKA MATH™

Lesson 24: Decompose and compose fractions greater than 1 to express them in various forms.

103

2. Convert each fraction to a mixed number. Show your work as in the example. Model with a number line.

a. $\frac{11}{3}$

$$\frac{11}{3} = \frac{3 \times 3}{3} + \frac{2}{3} = 3 + \frac{2}{3} = 3\frac{2}{3}$$

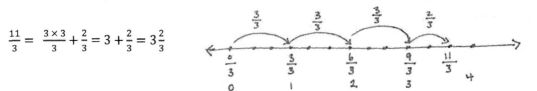

b. $\frac{13}{2}$

c. $\frac{18}{4}$

3. Convert each fraction to a mixed number.

a. $\frac{14}{3} =$	b. $\frac{17}{4} =$	c. $\frac{27}{5} =$
d. $\frac{28}{6} =$	e. $\frac{23}{7} =$	f. $\frac{37}{8} =$
g. $\frac{51}{9} =$	h. $\frac{74}{10} =$	i. $\frac{45}{12} =$

EUREKA MATH | Lesson 24: Decompose and compose fractions greater than 1 to express them in various forms.

Name _____   Date _____

1. Convert each mixed number to a fraction greater than 1. Draw a number line to model your work.

a. $3\frac{1}{4}$

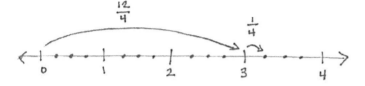

$$3\frac{1}{4} = 3 + \frac{1}{4} = \frac{12}{4} + \frac{1}{4} = \frac{13}{4}$$

b. $2\frac{4}{5}$

c. $3\frac{5}{8}$

d. $4\frac{4}{10}$

e. $4\frac{7}{9}$

EUREKA MATH

Lesson 25:   Decompose and compose fractions greater than 1 to express them in various forms.

105

2. Convert each mixed number to a fraction greater than 1. Show your work as in the example.
   (Note: $3 \times \frac{4}{4} = \frac{3 \times 4}{4}$)

a. $3\frac{3}{4}$

$$3\frac{3}{4} = 3 + \frac{3}{4} = \left(3 \times \frac{4}{4}\right) + \frac{3}{4} = \frac{12}{4} + \frac{3}{4} = \frac{15}{4}$$

b. $4\frac{1}{3}$

c. $4\frac{3}{5}$

d. $4\frac{6}{8}$

3. Convert each mixed number to a fraction greater than 1.

a. $2\frac{3}{4}$	b. $2\frac{2}{5}$	c. $3\frac{3}{6}$
d. $3\frac{3}{8}$	e. $3\frac{1}{10}$	f. $4\frac{3}{8}$
g. $5\frac{2}{3}$	h. $6\frac{1}{2}$	i. $7\frac{3}{10}$

Lesson 25:   Decompose and compose fractions greater than 1 to express them in various forms.

Name _____   Date _____

.. Convert each mixed number to a fraction greater than 1. Draw a number line to model your work.

a. $3\frac{1}{4}$

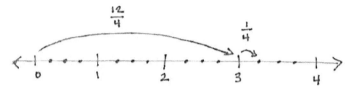

$3\frac{1}{4} = 3 + \frac{1}{4} = \frac{12}{4} + \frac{1}{4} = \frac{13}{4}$

b. $4\frac{2}{5}$

c. $5\frac{3}{8}$

d. $3\frac{7}{10}$

e. $6\frac{2}{9}$

EUREKA
MATH | Lesson 25:   Decompose and compose fractions greater than 1 to express them
                        in various forms.

107

2. Convert each mixed number to a fraction greater than 1. Show your work as in the example.
   (Note: $3 \times \frac{4}{4} = \frac{3 \times 4}{4}$)

   a. $3\frac{3}{4}$

   $$3\frac{3}{4} = 3 + \frac{3}{4} = \left(3 \times \frac{4}{4}\right) + \frac{3}{4} = \frac{12}{4} + \frac{3}{4} = \frac{15}{4}$$

   b. $5\frac{2}{3}$

   c. $4\frac{1}{5}$

   d. $3\frac{7}{8}$

3. Convert each mixed number to a fraction greater than 1.

a. $2\frac{1}{3}$	b. $2\frac{3}{4}$	c. $3\frac{2}{5}$
d. $3\frac{1}{6}$	e. $4\frac{5}{12}$	f. $4\frac{2}{5}$
g. $4\frac{1}{10}$	h. $5\frac{1}{5}$	i. $5\frac{5}{6}$
j. $6\frac{1}{4}$	k. $7\frac{1}{2}$	l. $7\frac{11}{12}$

EUREKA MATH   Lesson 25:   Decompose and compose fractions greater than 1 to express them in various forms.

Name _____   Date _____

a. Plot the following points on the number line without measuring.

    i. $2\frac{7}{8}$ ii. $3\frac{1}{6}$ iii. $\frac{29}{12}$

2   3   4

b. Use the number line in Problem 1(a) to compare the fractions by writing >, <, or =.

    i. $\frac{29}{12}$ _____ $2\frac{7}{8}$ ii. $\frac{29}{12}$ _____ $3\frac{1}{6}$

a. Plot the following points on the number line without measuring.

    i. $\frac{70}{9}$ ii. $8\frac{2}{4}$ iii. $\frac{25}{3}$

7   8   9

b. Compare the following by writing >, <, or =.

    i. $8\frac{2}{4}$ _____ $\frac{25}{3}$ ii. $\frac{70}{9}$ _____ $8\frac{2}{4}$

c. Explain how you plotted the points in Problem 2(a).

3. Compare the fractions given below by writing >, <, or =. Give a brief explanation for each answer, referring to benchmark fractions.

   a. $5\frac{1}{3}$ _____ $4\frac{3}{4}$

   b. $\frac{12}{6}$ _____ $\frac{25}{12}$

   c. $\frac{18}{7}$ _____ $\frac{17}{5}$

   d. $5\frac{2}{5}$ _____ $5\frac{5}{8}$

   e. $6\frac{2}{3}$ _____ $6\frac{3}{7}$

   f. $\frac{31}{7}$ _____ $\frac{32}{8}$

   g. $\frac{31}{10}$ _____ $\frac{25}{8}$

   h. $\frac{39}{12}$ _____ $\frac{19}{6}$

   i. $\frac{49}{50}$ _____ $3\frac{90}{100}$

   j. $5\frac{5}{12}$ _____ $5\frac{51}{100}$

Lesson 26:   Compare fractions greater than 1 by reasoning using benchmark fractions.

Name _____   Date _____

a. Plot the following points on the number line without measuring.

  i. $2\frac{1}{6}$ ii. $3\frac{3}{4}$ iii. $\frac{33}{9}$

2   3   4

b. Use the number line in Problem 1(a) to compare the fractions by writing >, <, or =.

  i. $\frac{33}{9}$ _____ $2\frac{1}{6}$ ii. $\frac{33}{9}$ _____ $3\frac{3}{4}$

2.

a. Plot the following points on the number line without measuring.

  i. $\frac{65}{8}$ ii. $8\frac{5}{6}$ iii. $\frac{29}{4}$

7   8   9

b. Compare the following by writing >, <, or =.

  i. $8\frac{5}{6}$ _____ $\frac{65}{8}$ ii. $\frac{29}{4}$ _____ $\frac{65}{8}$

c. Explain how you plotted the points in Problem 2(a).

EUREKA
MATH™   Lesson 26:   Compare fractions greater than 1 by reasoning using benchmark
                              fractions.

                                                                                111

3. Compare the fractions given below by writing >, <, or =. Give a brief explanation for each answer, referring to benchmark fractions.

a. $5\frac{1}{3}$ _____ $5\frac{3}{4}$

b. $\frac{12}{4}$ _____ $\frac{25}{8}$

c. $\frac{18}{6}$ _____ $\frac{17}{4}$

d. $5\frac{3}{5}$ _____ $5\frac{5}{10}$

e. $6\frac{3}{4}$ _____ $6\frac{3}{5}$

f. $\frac{33}{6}$ _____ $\frac{34}{7}$

g. $\frac{23}{10}$ _____ $\frac{20}{8}$

h. $\frac{27}{12}$ _____ $\frac{15}{6}$

i. $2\frac{49}{50}$ _____ $2\frac{99}{100}$

j. $6\frac{5}{9}$ _____ $6\frac{49}{100}$

EUREKA
MATH™

Lesson 26:   Compare fractions greater than 1 by reasoning using benchmark fractions.

Name _____   Date _____

. Draw a tape diagram to model each comparison. Use >, <, or = to compare.

a. $3\frac{2}{3}$ _____ $3\frac{5}{6}$

b. $3\frac{2}{5}$ _____ $3\frac{6}{10}$

c. $4\frac{3}{6}$ _____ $4\frac{1}{3}$

d. $4\frac{5}{8}$ _____ $\frac{19}{4}$

2. Use an area model to make like units. Then, use >, <, or = to compare.

a. $2\frac{3}{5}$ _____ $\frac{18}{7}$

b. $2\frac{3}{8}$ _____ $2\frac{1}{3}$

Lesson 27:   Compare fractions greater than 1 by creating common numerators
or denominators.

3. Compare each pair of fractions using >, <, or = using any strategy.

a. $5\frac{3}{4}$ _____ $5\frac{3}{8}$

b. $5\frac{2}{5}$ _____ $5\frac{8}{10}$

c. $5\frac{6}{10}$ _____ $\frac{27}{5}$

d. $5\frac{2}{3}$ _____ $5\frac{9}{15}$

e. $\frac{7}{2}$ _____ $\frac{7}{3}$

f. $\frac{12}{3}$ _____ $\frac{15}{4}$

g. $\frac{22}{5}$ _____ $4\frac{2}{7}$

h. $\frac{21}{4}$ _____ $5\frac{2}{5}$

i. $\frac{29}{8}$ _____ $\frac{11}{3}$

j. $3\frac{3}{4}$ _____ $3\frac{4}{7}$

EUREKA MATH

Lesson 27: Compare fractions greater than 1 by creating common numerators or denominators.

Name _____   Date _____

1. Draw a tape diagram to model each comparison. Use >, <, or = to compare.

   a. $2\frac{3}{4}$ _____ $2\frac{7}{8}$

   b. $10\frac{2}{6}$ _____ $10\frac{1}{3}$

   c. $5\frac{3}{8}$ _____ $5\frac{1}{4}$

   d. $2\frac{5}{9}$ _____ $\frac{21}{3}$

2. Use an area model to make like units. Then, use >, <, or = to compare.

   a. $2\frac{4}{5}$ _____ $\frac{11}{4}$

   b. $2\frac{3}{5}$ _____ $2\frac{2}{3}$

EUREKA
MATH

Lesson 27: Compare fractions greater than 1 by creating common numerators
or denominators.

115

3. Compare each pair of fractions using >, <, or = using any strategy.

a. $6\frac{1}{2}$ _____ $6\frac{3}{8}$ b. $7\frac{5}{6}$ _____ $7\frac{11}{12}$

c. $3\frac{6}{10}$ _____ $3\frac{2}{5}$ d. $2\frac{2}{5}$ _____ $2\frac{8}{15}$

e. $\frac{10}{3}$ _____ $\frac{10}{4}$ f. $\frac{12}{4}$ _____ $\frac{10}{3}$

g. $\frac{38}{9}$ _____ $4\frac{2}{12}$ h. $\frac{23}{4}$ _____ $5\frac{2}{3}$

i. $\frac{30}{8}$ _____ $3\frac{7}{12}$ j. $10\frac{3}{4}$ _____ $10\frac{4}{6}$

Lesson 27:   Compare fractions greater than 1 by creating common numerators
or denominators.

Name _____ Date _____

. The chart to the right shows the distance fourth graders in Ms. Smith's class were able to run before stopping for a rest. Create a line plot to display the data in the table.

Student	Distance (in miles)
Joe	$2\frac{1}{2}$
Arianna	$1\frac{3}{4}$
Bobbi	$2\frac{1}{8}$
Morgan	$1\frac{5}{8}$
Jack	$2\frac{5}{8}$
Saisha	$2\frac{1}{4}$
Tyler	$2\frac{2}{4}$
Jenny	$\frac{5}{8}$
Anson	$2\frac{2}{8}$
Chandra	$2\frac{4}{8}$

2. Solve each problem.

   a. Who ran a mile farther than Jenny?

   b. Who ran a mile less than Jack?

   c. Two students ran exactly $2\frac{1}{4}$ miles. Identify the students. How many quarter miles did each student run?

   d. What is the difference, in miles, between the longest and shortest distance run?

   e. Compare the distances run by Arianna and Morgan using >, <, or =.

   f. Ms. Smith ran twice as far as Jenny. How far did Ms. Smith run? Write her distance as a mixed number.

   g. Mr. Reynolds ran $1\frac{3}{10}$ miles. Use >, <, or = to compare the distance Mr. Reynolds ran to the distance that Ms. Smith ran. Who ran farther?

3. Using the information in the table and on the line plot, develop and write a question similar to those above. Solve, and then ask your partner to solve. Did you solve in the same way? Did you get the same answer?

Name _____   Date _____

. A group of children measured the lengths of their shoes. The measurements are shown in the table. Make a line plot to display the data.

Students	Length of Shoe (in inches)
Collin	$8\frac{1}{2}$
Dickon	$7\frac{3}{4}$
Ben	$7\frac{1}{2}$
Martha	$7\frac{3}{4}$
Lilias	8
Susan	$8\frac{1}{2}$
Frances	$7\frac{3}{4}$
Mary	$8\frac{3}{4}$

2. Solve each problem.

a. Who has a shoe length 1 inch longer than Dickon?

b. Who has a shoe length 1 inch shorter than Susan?

c. How many quarter inches long is Martha's shoe length?

d. What is the difference, in inches, between Lilias's and Martha's shoe lengths?

e. Compare the shoe length of Ben and Frances using >, <, or =.

f. How many students had shoes that measured less than 8 inches?

g. How many children measured the length of their shoes?

h. Mr. Jones's shoe length was $\frac{25}{2}$ inches. Use >, <, or = to compare the length of Mr. Jones's shoe to the length of the longest student shoe length. Who had the longer shoe?

3. Using the information in the table and on the line plot, write a question you could solve by using the line plot. Solve.

Name _____   Date _____

1. Estimate each sum or difference to the nearest half or whole number by rounding. Explain your estimate using words or a number line.

   a. $2\frac{1}{12} + 1\frac{7}{8} \approx$ _____

   b. $1\frac{11}{12} + 5\frac{3}{4} \approx$ _____

   c. $8\frac{7}{8} - 2\frac{1}{9} \approx$ _____

   d. $6\frac{1}{8} - 2\frac{1}{12} \approx$ _____

   e. $3\frac{3}{8} + 5\frac{1}{9} \approx$ _____

2. Estimate each sum or difference to the nearest half or whole number by rounding. Explain your estimate using words or a number line.

   a. $\frac{16}{5} + \frac{11}{4} \approx$ _____

   b. $\frac{17}{3} - \frac{15}{7} \approx$ _____

   c. $\frac{59}{10} + \frac{26}{10} \approx$ _____

3. Montoya's estimate for $8\frac{5}{8} - 2\frac{1}{3}$ was 7. Julio's estimate was $6\frac{1}{2}$. Whose estimate do you think is closer to the actual difference? Explain.

4. Use benchmark numbers or mental math to estimate the sum or difference.

a. $14\frac{3}{4} + 29\frac{11}{12}$	b. $3\frac{5}{12} + 54\frac{5}{8}$
c. $17\frac{4}{5} - 8\frac{7}{12}$	d. $\frac{65}{8} - \frac{37}{6}$

Name _____   Date _____

Estimate each sum or difference to the nearest half or whole number by rounding. Explain your estimate using words or a number line.

a. $3\frac{1}{10} + 1\frac{3}{4} \approx$ _____

b. $2\frac{9}{10} + 4\frac{4}{5} \approx$ _____

c. $9\frac{9}{10} - 5\frac{1}{5} \approx$ _____

d. $4\frac{1}{9} - 1\frac{1}{10} \approx$ _____

e. $6\frac{3}{12} + 5\frac{1}{9} \approx$ _____

2. Estimate each sum or difference to the nearest half or whole number by rounding. Explain your estimate using words or a number line.

   a. $\frac{16}{3} + \frac{17}{8} \approx$ _____

   b. $\frac{17}{3} - \frac{15}{4} \approx$ _____

   c. $\frac{57}{8} + \frac{26}{8} \approx$ _____

3. Gina's estimate for $7\frac{5}{8} - 2\frac{1}{2}$ was 5. Dominick's estimate was $5\frac{1}{2}$. Whose estimate do you think is closer to the actual difference? Explain.

4. Use benchmark numbers or mental math to estimate the sum or difference.

a. $10\frac{3}{4} + 12\frac{11}{12}$	b. $2\frac{7}{10} + 23\frac{3}{8}$
c. $15\frac{9}{12} - 8\frac{11}{12}$	d. $\frac{56}{7} - \frac{31}{8}$

Name _____   Date _____

1. Solve.

   a. $3\frac{1}{4} + \frac{1}{4}$

   b. $7\frac{3}{4} + \frac{1}{4}$

   c. $\frac{3}{8} + 5\frac{2}{8}$

   d. $\frac{1}{8} + 6\frac{7}{8}$

2. Complete the number sentences.

a. $4\frac{7}{8} +$ ____ $= 5$	b. $7\frac{2}{5} +$ ____ $= 8$
c. $3 = 2\frac{1}{6} +$ ____	d. $12 = 11\frac{1}{12} +$ ____

3. Use a number bond and the arrow way to show how to make one. Solve.

   a. $2\frac{3}{4} + \frac{2}{4}$

   $\frac{1}{4}$ $\frac{1}{4}$

   b. $3\frac{3}{5} + \frac{3}{5}$

4. Solve.

a. $4\frac{2}{3} + \frac{2}{3}$	b. $3\frac{3}{5} + \frac{4}{5}$
c. $5\frac{4}{6} + \frac{5}{6}$	d. $\frac{7}{8} + 6\frac{4}{8}$
e. $\frac{7}{10} + 7\frac{9}{10}$	f. $9\frac{7}{12} + \frac{11}{12}$
g. $2\frac{70}{100} + \frac{87}{100}$	h. $\frac{50}{100} + 16\frac{78}{100}$

5. To solve $7\frac{9}{10} + \frac{5}{10}$, Maria thought, "$7\frac{9}{10} + \frac{1}{10} = 8$ and $8 + \frac{4}{10} = 8\frac{4}{10}$."

Paul thought, "$7\frac{9}{10} + \frac{5}{10} = 7\frac{14}{10} = 7 + \frac{10}{10} + \frac{4}{10} = 8\frac{4}{10}$." Explain why Maria and Paul are both right.

Name _____   Date _____

. Solve.

a. $4\frac{1}{3} + \frac{1}{3}$

b. $5\frac{1}{4} + \frac{2}{4}$

c. $\frac{2}{6} + 3\frac{4}{6}$

d. $\frac{5}{8} + 7\frac{3}{8}$

. Complete the number sentences.

a. $3\frac{5}{6} +$ ____ $= 4$	b. $5\frac{3}{7} +$ ____ $= 6$
c. $5 = 4\frac{1}{8} +$ ____	d. $15 = 14\frac{4}{12} +$ ____

3. Draw a number bond and the arrow way to show how to make one. Solve.

a. $2\frac{4}{5} + \frac{2}{5}$

b. $3\frac{2}{3} + \frac{2}{3}$

c. $4\frac{4}{6} + \frac{5}{6}$

$\frac{1}{5}$ $\frac{1}{5}$

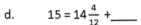

$2\frac{4}{5} \xrightarrow{+\frac{1}{5}} 3 \xrightarrow{+\frac{1}{5}} 3\frac{1}{5}$

4. Solve.

a. $2\frac{3}{5} + \frac{3}{5}$	b. $3\frac{6}{8} + \frac{4}{8}$
c. $5\frac{4}{6} + \frac{3}{6}$	d. $\frac{7}{10} + 6\frac{6}{10}$
e. $\frac{5}{10} + 8\frac{9}{10}$	f. $7\frac{8}{12} + \frac{11}{12}$
g. $3\frac{90}{100} + \frac{58}{100}$	h. $\frac{60}{100} + 14\frac{79}{100}$

5. To solve $4\frac{8}{10} + \frac{3}{10}$, Carmen thought, "$4\frac{8}{10} + \frac{2}{10} = 5$, and $5 + \frac{1}{10} = 5\frac{1}{10}$."

   Benny thought, "$4\frac{8}{10} + \frac{3}{10} = 4\frac{11}{10} = 4 + \frac{10}{10} + \frac{1}{10} = 5\frac{1}{10}$." Explain why Carmen and Benny are both right.

Name _____   Date _____

1. Solve.

a. $3\frac{1}{3}$ + $2\frac{2}{3}$ = 5 + $\frac{3}{3}$ =

```
   3      1        2       2
         ───              ───
          3                3
```

b. $4\frac{1}{4} + 3\frac{2}{4}$

c. $2\frac{2}{6} + 6\frac{4}{6}$

2. Solve. Use a number line to show your work.

a. $2\frac{4}{5} + 1\frac{2}{5}$ = 3 + $\frac{6}{5}$ = _____

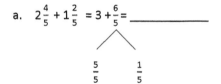

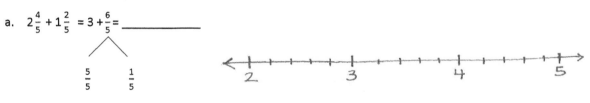

b. $1\frac{3}{4} + 3\frac{3}{4}$

c. $3\frac{3}{8} + 2\frac{6}{8}$

3. Solve. Use the arrow way to show how to make one.

a. $2\frac{4}{6} + 1\frac{5}{6} = 3\frac{4}{6} + \frac{5}{6} =$

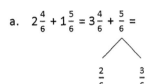

$\frac{2}{6} \qquad \frac{3}{6}$

b. $1\frac{3}{4} + 3\frac{3}{4}$

c. $3\frac{3}{8} + 2\frac{6}{8}$

4. Solve. Use whichever method you prefer.

a. $1\frac{3}{5} + 3\frac{4}{5}$

b. $2\frac{6}{8} + 3\frac{7}{8}$

c. $3\frac{8}{12} + 2\frac{7}{12}$

Name _____   Date _____

1. Solve.

    a. $2\frac{1}{3}$ + $1\frac{2}{3}$ = 3 + $\frac{3}{3}$ =

    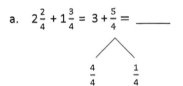

    b. $2\frac{2}{5}$ + $2\frac{2}{5}$

    c. $3\frac{3}{8}$ + $1\frac{5}{8}$

2. Solve. Use a number line to show your work.

    a. $2\frac{2}{4} + 1\frac{3}{4} = 3 + \frac{5}{4} =$ _____

    b. $3\frac{4}{6} + 2\frac{5}{6}$

    c. $1\frac{9}{12} + 1\frac{7}{12}$

3. Solve. Use the arrow way to show how to make one.

    a. $2\frac{3}{4} + 1\frac{3}{4} = 3\frac{3}{4} + \frac{3}{4} =$

$$\frac{1}{4} \qquad \frac{2}{4}$$

$$3\frac{3}{4} \xrightarrow{+\frac{1}{4}} 4 \longrightarrow$$

    b. $2\frac{7}{8} + 3\frac{4}{8}$

    c. $1\frac{7}{9} + 4\frac{5}{9}$

4. Solve. Use whichever method you prefer.

    a. $1\frac{4}{5} + 1\frac{3}{5}$

    b. $3\frac{8}{10} + 1\frac{5}{10}$

    c. $2\frac{5}{7} + 3\frac{6}{7}$

Name _____   Date _____

. Subtract. Model with a number line or the arrow way.

a. $3\frac{3}{4} - \frac{1}{4}$

b. $4\frac{7}{10} - \frac{3}{10}$

c. $5\frac{1}{3} - \frac{2}{3}$

d. $9\frac{3}{5} - \frac{4}{5}$

2. Use decomposition to subtract the fractions. Model with a number line or the arrow way.

a. $5\frac{3}{5} - \frac{4}{5}$

$\frac{3}{5}$ $\frac{1}{5}$

b. $4\frac{1}{4} - \frac{2}{4}$

c. $5\frac{1}{3} - \frac{2}{3}$

d. $2\frac{3}{8} - \frac{5}{8}$

EUREKA MATH   **Lesson 32:**   Subtract a fraction from a mixed number.

133

3. Decompose the total to subtract the fractions.

a. $3\frac{1}{8} - \frac{3}{8} = 2\frac{1}{8} + \frac{5}{8} = 2\frac{6}{8}$

$2\frac{1}{8}$ ⌃ 1

b. $5\frac{1}{8} - \frac{7}{8}$

c. $5\frac{3}{5} - \frac{4}{5}$

d. $5\frac{4}{6} - \frac{5}{6}$

e. $6\frac{4}{12} - \frac{7}{12}$

f. $9\frac{1}{8} - \frac{5}{8}$

g. $7\frac{1}{6} - \frac{5}{6}$

h. $8\frac{3}{10} - \frac{4}{10}$

i. $12\frac{3}{5} - \frac{4}{5}$

j. $11\frac{2}{6} - \frac{5}{6}$

Name _____   Date _____

. Subtract. Model with a number line or the arrow way.

a. $6\frac{3}{5} - \frac{1}{5}$

b. $4\frac{9}{12} - \frac{7}{12}$

c. $7\frac{1}{4} - \frac{3}{4}$

d. $8\frac{3}{8} - \frac{5}{8}$

2. Use decomposition to subtract the fractions. Model with a number line or the arrow way.

a. $2\frac{2}{5} - \frac{4}{5}$

$\frac{2}{5}$ $\frac{2}{5}$

b. $2\frac{1}{3} - \frac{2}{3}$

c. $4\frac{1}{6} - \frac{4}{6}$

d. $3\frac{3}{6} - \frac{5}{6}$

| **Lesson 32:**   Subtract a fraction from a mixed number.

e. $9\frac{3}{8} - \frac{7}{8}$

f. $7\frac{1}{10} - \frac{6}{10}$

g. $10\frac{1}{8} - \frac{5}{8}$

h. $9\frac{4}{12} - \frac{7}{12}$

i. $11\frac{3}{5} - \frac{4}{5}$

j. $17\frac{1}{9} - \frac{5}{9}$

3. Decompose the total to subtract the fractions.

a. $4\frac{1}{8} - \frac{3}{8} = 3\frac{1}{8} + \frac{5}{8} = 3\frac{6}{8}$

$3\frac{1}{8}$ ⌃ 1

b. $5\frac{2}{5} - \frac{3}{5}$

c. $7\frac{1}{8} - \frac{3}{8}$

d. $3\frac{3}{9} - \frac{4}{9}$

e. $6\frac{3}{10} - \frac{7}{10}$

f. $2\frac{5}{9} - \frac{8}{9}$

Name _____   Date _____

. Write a related addition sentence. Subtract by counting on. Use a number line or the arrow way to help. The first one has been partially done for you.

a. $3\frac{1}{3} - 1\frac{2}{3} =$ _____

$1\frac{2}{3} +$ _____ $= 3\frac{1}{3}$

b. $5\frac{1}{4} - 2\frac{3}{4} =$ _____

. Subtract, as shown in Problem 2(a), by decomposing the fractional part of the number you are subtracting. Use a number line or the arrow way to help you.

a. $3\frac{1}{4} - 1\frac{3}{4} = 2\frac{1}{4} - \frac{3}{4} = 1\frac{2}{4}$

$\overset{\displaystyle\frown}{}$

$\frac{1}{4} \qquad \frac{2}{4}$

b. $4\frac{1}{5} - 2\frac{4}{5}$

c. $5\frac{3}{7} - 3\frac{6}{7}$

EUREKA
MATH   Lesson 33:   Subtract a mixed number from a mixed number.

137

3. Subtract, as shown in Problem 3(a), by decomposing to take one out.

   a. $5\frac{3}{5} - 2\frac{4}{5} = 3\frac{3}{5} - \frac{4}{5}$

   $$2\frac{3}{5} \qquad 1$$

   b. $4\frac{3}{6} - 3\frac{5}{6}$

   c. $8\frac{3}{10} - 2\frac{7}{10}$

4. Solve using any method.

   a. $6\frac{1}{4} - 3\frac{3}{4}$ b. $5\frac{1}{8} - 2\frac{7}{8}$

   c. $8\frac{3}{12} - 3\frac{8}{12}$ d. $5\frac{1}{100} - 2\frac{97}{100}$

Name _____   Date _____

. Write a related addition sentence. Subtract by counting on. Use a number line or the arrow way to help. The first one has been partially done for you.

a. $3\frac{2}{5} - 1\frac{4}{5} =$ _____

$1\frac{4}{5} +$ _____ $= 3\frac{2}{5}$

b. $5\frac{3}{8} - 2\frac{5}{8}$

. Subtract, as shown in Problem 2(a) below, by decomposing the fractional part of the number you are subtracting. Use a number line or the arrow way to help you.

a. $4\frac{1}{5} - 1\frac{3}{5} = 3\frac{1}{5} - \frac{3}{5} = 2\frac{3}{5}$

$\frac{1}{5} \qquad \frac{2}{5}$

b. $4\frac{1}{7} - 2\frac{4}{7}$

c. $5\frac{5}{12} - 3\frac{8}{12}$

2. Subtract, as shown in 3(a) below, by decomposing to take one out.

    a. $5\frac{5}{8} - 2\frac{7}{8} = 3\frac{5}{8} - \frac{7}{8} =$

$$2\frac{5}{8} \qquad 1$$

    b. $4\frac{3}{12} - 3\frac{8}{12}$

    c. $9\frac{1}{10} - 6\frac{9}{10}$

3. Solve using any strategy.

    a. $6\frac{1}{9} - 4\frac{3}{9}$ b. $5\frac{3}{10} - 3\frac{6}{10}$

    c. $8\frac{7}{12} - 5\frac{9}{12}$ d. $7\frac{4}{100} - 2\frac{92}{100}$

Lesson 33:   Subtract a mixed number from a mixed number.

Name _____   Date _____

. Subtract.

a. $4\frac{1}{3} - \frac{2}{3}$

3          $\frac{4}{3}$

b. $5\frac{2}{4} - \frac{3}{4}$

c. $8\frac{3}{5} - \frac{4}{5}$

2. Subtract the ones first.

a. $3\frac{1}{4} - 1\frac{3}{4} = 2\frac{1}{4} - \frac{3}{4} = 1\frac{2}{4}$

1          $\frac{5}{4}$

b. $4\frac{2}{5} - 1\frac{3}{5}$

c. $5\frac{2}{6} - 3\frac{5}{6}$

d. $9\frac{3}{5} - 2\frac{4}{5}$

3. Solve using any strategy.

a. $7\frac{3}{8} - 2\frac{5}{8}$ b. $6\frac{4}{10} - 3\frac{8}{10}$

c. $8\frac{3}{12} - 3\frac{8}{12}$ d. $14\frac{2}{50} - 6\frac{43}{50}$

Name _____   Date _____

1. Subtract.

   a. $5\frac{1}{4} - \frac{3}{4}$

   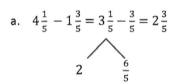

   b. $6\frac{3}{8} - \frac{6}{8}$

   c. $7\frac{4}{6} - \frac{5}{6}$

2. Subtract the ones first.

   a. $4\frac{1}{5} - 1\frac{3}{5} = 3\frac{1}{5} - \frac{3}{5} = 2\frac{3}{5}$

   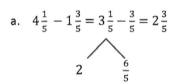

   b. $4\frac{3}{6} - 2\frac{5}{6}$

c. $8\frac{3}{8} - 2\frac{5}{8}$

d. $13\frac{3}{10} - 8\frac{7}{10}$

3. Solve using any strategy.

   a. $7\frac{3}{12} - 4\frac{9}{12}$ b. $9\frac{6}{10} - 5\frac{8}{10}$

   c. $17\frac{2}{16} - 9\frac{7}{16}$ d. $12\frac{5}{100} - 8\frac{94}{100}$

Name _____   Date _____

1. Draw and label a tape diagram to show the following are true.

   a. 8 fifths = 4 × (2 fifths) = (4 × 2) fifths

   b. 10 sixths = 5 × (2 sixths) = (5 × 2) sixths

2. Write the expression in unit form to solve.

   a. $7 \times \frac{2}{3}$

   b. $4 \times \frac{2}{4}$

   c. $16 \times \frac{3}{8}$

   d. $6 \times \frac{5}{8}$

EUREKA
MATH™

Lesson 35:   Represent the multiplication of n times a/b as (n × a)/b using the
             associative property and visual models.

145

3. Solve.

a. $7 \times \frac{4}{9}$

b. $6 \times \frac{3}{5}$

c. $8 \times \frac{3}{4}$

d. $16 \times \frac{3}{8}$

e. $12 \times \frac{7}{10}$

f. $3 \times \frac{54}{100}$

4. Maria needs $\frac{3}{5}$ yard of fabric for each costume. How many yards of fabric does she need for 6 costumes?

Name _____   Date _____

1. Draw and label a tape diagram to show the following are true.

   a. 8 thirds = 4 × (2 thirds) = (4 × 2) thirds

   b. 15 eighths = 3 × (5 eighths) = (3 × 5) eighths

2. Write the expression in unit form to solve.

   a. $10 \times \frac{2}{5}$ b. $3 \times \frac{5}{6}$

   c. $9 \times \frac{4}{9}$ d. $7 \times \frac{3}{4}$

EUREKA
MATH™   Lesson 35:   Represent the multiplication of n times a/b as (n × a)/b using the
                             associative property and visual models.
                                                                                          147

3. Solve.

a. $6 \times \frac{3}{4}$

b. $7 \times \frac{5}{8}$

c. $13 \times \frac{2}{3}$

d. $18 \times \frac{2}{3}$

e. $14 \times \frac{7}{10}$

f. $7 \times \frac{14}{100}$

4. Mrs. Smith bought some orange juice. Each member of her family drank $\frac{2}{3}$ cup for breakfast. There are five people in her family. How many cups of orange juice did they drink?

EUREKA MATH™

Lesson 35:   Represent the multiplication of n times a/b as (n × a)/b using the associative property and visual models.

ame _____   Date _____

. Draw a tape diagram to represent
$\frac{3}{4} + \frac{3}{4} + \frac{3}{4} + \frac{3}{4}$.

2. Draw a tape diagram to represent
$\frac{7}{12} + \frac{7}{12} + \frac{7}{12}$.

Write a multiplication expression equal to
$\frac{3}{4} + \frac{3}{4} + \frac{3}{4} + \frac{3}{4}$.

Write a multiplication expression equal to
$\frac{7}{12} + \frac{7}{12} + \frac{7}{12}$

3. Rewrite each repeated addition problem as a multiplication problem and solve. Express the result as a mixed number. The first one has been started for you.

a. $\frac{7}{5} + \frac{7}{5} + \frac{7}{5} + \frac{7}{5} = 4 \times \frac{7}{5} = \frac{4 \times 7}{5} =$

b. $\frac{9}{10} + \frac{9}{10} + \frac{9}{10}$

c. $\frac{11}{12} + \frac{11}{12} + \frac{11}{12} + \frac{11}{12} + \frac{11}{12}$

EUREKA
MATH™

Lesson 36:   Represent the multiplication of n times a/b as $(n \times a)/b$ using the
associative property and visual models.

149

4. Solve using any method. Express your answers as whole or mixed numbers.

   a. $8 \times \frac{2}{3}$ b. $12 \times \frac{3}{4}$

   c. $50 \times \frac{4}{5}$ d. $26 \times \frac{7}{8}$

5. Morgan poured $\frac{9}{10}$ liter of punch into each of 6 bottles. How many liters of punch did she pour in all?

6. A recipe calls for $\frac{3}{4}$ cup rice. How many cups of rice are needed to make the recipe 14 times?

7. A butcher prepared 120 sausages using $\frac{3}{8}$ pound of meat for each. How many pounds did he use in all?

EUREKA
MATH

Lesson 36:   Represent the multiplication of n times a/b as (n × a)/b using the
associative property and visual models.

Name _____   Date _____

1. Draw a tape diagram to represent

   $\frac{2}{3}+\frac{2}{3}+\frac{2}{3}+\frac{2}{3}.$

2. Draw a tape diagram to represent

   $\frac{7}{8}+\frac{7}{8}+\frac{7}{8}.$

Write a multiplication expression equal to

$\frac{2}{3}+\frac{2}{3}+\frac{2}{3}+\frac{2}{3}.$

Write a multiplication expression equal to

$\frac{7}{8}+\frac{7}{8}+\frac{7}{8}.$

3. Rewrite each repeated addition problem as a multiplication problem and solve. Express the result as a mixed number. The first one has been completed for you.

   a. $\frac{7}{5}+\frac{7}{5}+\frac{7}{5}+\frac{7}{5}=4\times\frac{7}{5}=\frac{4\times7}{5}=\frac{28}{5}=5\frac{3}{5}$

   b. $\frac{7}{10}+\frac{7}{10}+\frac{7}{10}$

   c. $\frac{5}{12}+\frac{5}{12}+\frac{5}{12}+\frac{5}{12}+\frac{5}{12}+\frac{5}{12}$

   d. $\frac{3}{8}+\frac{3}{8}+\frac{3}{8}+\frac{3}{8}+\frac{3}{8}+\frac{3}{8}+\frac{3}{8}+\frac{3}{8}+\frac{3}{8}+\frac{3}{8}+\frac{3}{8}$

4. Solve using any method. Express your answers as whole or mixed numbers.

   a. $7\times\frac{2}{9}$

   b. $11\times\frac{2}{3}$

EUREKA MATH™

Lesson 36: Represent the multiplication of n times a/b as (n × a)/b using the associative property and visual models.

151

c. $40 \times \frac{2}{6}$

d. $24 \times \frac{5}{6}$

e. $23 \times \frac{3}{5}$

f. $34 \times \frac{2}{8}$

5. Coleton is playing with interlocking blocks that are each $\frac{3}{4}$ inch tall. He makes a tower 17 blocks tall. How tall is his tower in inches?

6. There were 11 players on Mr. Maiorani's softball team. They each ate $\frac{3}{8}$ of a pizza. How many pizzas did they eat?

7. A bricklayer places 12 bricks along an outside wall of a shed. Each brick is $\frac{3}{4}$ foot long. How many feet long is that wall of the shed?

EUREKA
MATH™   Lesson 36:   Represent the multiplication of n times a/b as (n × a)/b using the
                               associative property and visual models.

ame _____   Date _____

Draw tape diagrams to show two ways to represent 2 units of $4\frac{2}{3}$.

Write a multiplication expression to match each tape diagram.

Solve the following using the distributive property. The first one has been done for you. (As soon as you are ready, you may omit the step that is in line 2.)

a. $3 \times 6\frac{4}{5} = 3 \times \left(6 + \frac{4}{5}\right)$ $\qquad = (3 \times 6) + \left(3 \times \frac{4}{5}\right)$ $\qquad = 18 + \frac{12}{5}$ $\qquad = 18 + 2\frac{2}{5}$ $\qquad = 20\frac{2}{5}$	b. $2 \times 4\frac{2}{3}$
c. $3 \times 2\frac{5}{8}$	d. $2 \times 4\frac{7}{10}$

EUREKA MATH™

Lesson 37: Find the product of a whole number and a mixed number using the distributive property.

153

e. $3 \times 7\frac{3}{4}$	f. $6 \times 3\frac{1}{2}$
g. $4 \times 9\frac{1}{5}$	h. $5\frac{6}{8} \times 4$

3. For one dance costume, Saisha needs $4\frac{2}{3}$ feet of ribbon. How much ribbon does she need for 5 identical costumes?

ame _____   Date _____

1. Draw tape diagrams to show two ways to represent 3 units of $5\frac{1}{12}$.

Write a multiplication expression to match each tape diagram.

2. Solve the following using the distributive property. The first one has been done for you. (As soon as you are ready, you may omit the step that is in line 2.)

a. $3 \times 6\frac{4}{5} = 3 \times \left(6+\frac{4}{5}\right)$ $= (3 \times 6) + \left(3 \times \frac{4}{5}\right)$ $= 18 + \frac{12}{5}$ $= 18 + 2\frac{2}{5}$ $= 20\frac{2}{5}$	b. $5 \times 4\frac{1}{6}$
c. $6 \times 2\frac{3}{5}$	d. $2 \times 7\frac{3}{10}$

EUREKA MATH

Lesson 37: Find the product of a whole number and a mixed number using the distributive property.

155

e. $8 \times 7\frac{1}{4}$	f. $3\frac{3}{8} \times 12$

3. Sara's street is $2\frac{3}{10}$ miles long. She ran the length of the street 6 times. How far did she run?

4. Kelly's new puppy weighed $4\frac{7}{10}$ pounds when she brought him home. Now, he weighs six times as much. How much does he weigh now?

ame _____   Date _____

. Fill in the unknown factors.

a. $7 \times 3\frac{4}{5} = (\underline{\quad} \times 3) + (\underline{\quad} \times \frac{4}{5})$

b. $3 \times 12\frac{7}{8} = (3 \times \underline{\quad}) + (3 \times \underline{\quad})$

. Multiply. Use the distributive property.

a. $7 \times 8\frac{2}{5}$

b. $4\frac{5}{6} \times 9$

c. $3 \times 8\frac{11}{12}$

d. $5 \times 20\frac{8}{10}$

EUREKA
MATH™

Lesson 38:   Find the product of a whole number and a mixed number using the
distributive property.

157

e. $25\frac{4}{100} \times 4$

3.   The distance around the park is $2\frac{5}{10}$ miles. Cecilia ran around the park 3 times. How far did she run?

4.   Windsor the dog ate $4\frac{3}{4}$ snack bones each day for a week. How many bones did Windsor eat that week?

Name _____   Date _____

1. Fill in the unknown factors.

   a. $8 \times 4\frac{4}{7} = (\underline{} \times 4) + (\underline{} \times \frac{4}{7})$

   b. $9 \times 7\frac{7}{10} = (9 \times \underline{}) + (9 \times \underline{})$

2. Multiply. Use the distributive property.

   a. $6 \times 8\frac{2}{7}$

   b. $7\frac{3}{4} \times 9$

   c. $9 \times 8\frac{7}{9}$

   d. $25\frac{7}{8} \times 3$

EUREKA MATH™   Lesson 38:   Find the product of a whole number and a mixed number using the distributive property.

159

e. $4 \times 20\frac{8}{12}$

f. $30\frac{3}{100} \times 12$

3. Brandon is cutting 9 boards for a woodworking project. Each board is $4\frac{5}{8}$ feet long. What is the total length of the boards?

4. Rocky the collie ate $3\frac{1}{4}$ cups of dog food each day for two weeks. How much dog food did Rocky eat in that time?

5. At the class party, each student will be given a container that holds $8\frac{5}{8}$ ounces of juice. There are 25 students in the class. If each student's container is filled, how many ounces of juice does the teacher need to buy?

EUREKA
MATH

Lesson 38:   Find the product of a whole number and a mixed number using the
              distributive property.

Name _____   Date _____

Use the RDW process to solve.

1. Tameka ran $2\frac{5}{8}$ miles. Her sister ran twice as far. How far did Tameka's sister run?

2. Natasha's sculpture was $5\frac{3}{16}$ inches tall. Maya's was 4 times as tall. How much shorter was Natasha's sculpture than Maya's?

3. A seamstress needs $1\frac{5}{8}$ yards of fabric to make a child's dress. She needs 3 times as much fabric to make a woman's dress. How many yards of fabric does she need for both dresses?

4. A piece of blue yarn is $5\frac{2}{3}$ yards long. A piece of pink yarn is 5 times as long as the blue yarn. Bailey tied them together with a knot that used $\frac{1}{3}$ yard from each piece of yarn. What is the total length of the yarn tied together?

5. A truck driver drove $35\frac{2}{10}$ miles before he stopped for breakfast. He then drove 5 times as far before he stopped for lunch. How far did he drive that day before his lunch break?

6. Mr. Washington's motorcycle needs $5\frac{5}{10}$ gallons of gas to fill the tank. His van needs 5 times as much gas to fill it. If Mr. Washington pays \$3 per gallon for gas, how much will it cost him to fill both the motorcycle and the van?

Name _____   Date _____

Use the RDW process to solve.

1. Ground turkey is sold in packages of $2\frac{1}{2}$ pounds. Dawn bought eight times as much turkey that is sold in 1 package for her son's birthday party. How many pounds of ground turkey did Dawn buy?

2. Trevor's stack of books is $7\frac{7}{8}$ inches tall. Rick's stack is 3 times as tall. What is the difference in the heights of their stacks of books?

3. It takes $8\frac{3}{4}$ yards of fabric to make one quilt. Gail needs three times as much fabric to make three quilts. She already has two yards of fabric. How many more yards of fabric does Gail need to buy in order to make three quilts?

4. Carol made punch. She used $12\frac{3}{8}$ cups of juice and then added three times as much ginger ale. Then, she added 1 cup of lemonade. How many cups of punch did her recipe make?

5. Brandon drove $72\frac{7}{10}$ miles on Monday. He drove 3 times as far on Tuesday. How far did he drive in the two days?

6. Mrs. Reiser used $9\frac{8}{10}$ gallons of gas this week. Mr. Reiser used five times as much gas as Mrs. Reiser used this week. If Mr. Reiser pays $3 for each gallon of gas, how much did Mr. Reiser pay for gas this week?

ame _____   Date _____

. The chart to the right shows the height of some football players.

a. Use the data to create a line plot at the bottom of this page and to answer the questions below.

b. What is the difference in height of the tallest and shortest players?

c. Player I and Player B have a combined height that is $1\frac{1}{8}$ feet taller than a school bus. What is the height of a school bus?

Player	Height (in feet)
A	$6\frac{1}{4}$
B	$5\frac{7}{8}$
C	$6\frac{1}{2}$
D	$6\frac{1}{4}$
E	$6\frac{2}{8}$
F	$5\frac{7}{8}$
G	$6\frac{1}{8}$
H	$6\frac{5}{8}$
I	$5\frac{6}{8}$
J	$6\frac{1}{8}$

EUREKA MATH™   Lesson 40:   Solve word problems involving the multiplication of a whole number and a fraction including those involving line plots.

165

2. One of the players on the team is now 4 times as tall as he was at birth, when he measured $1\frac{5}{8}$ feet. Who is the player?

3. Six of the players on the team weigh over 300 pounds. Doctors recommend that players of this weight drink at least $3\frac{3}{4}$ quarts of water each day. At least how much water should be consumed per day by all 6 players?

4. Nine of the players on the team weigh about 200 pounds. Doctors recommend that people of this weight each eat about $7\frac{7}{10}$ grams of protein per pound each day. About how many combined grams of protein should these 9 players eat per day?

Name _____   Date _____

The chart to the right shows the total monthly rainfall for a city.

. Use the data to create a line plot at the bottom of this page and to answer the following questions.

Month	Rainfall (in inches)
January	$2\frac{2}{8}$
February	$1\frac{3}{8}$
March	$2\frac{3}{8}$
April	$2\frac{5}{8}$
May	$4\frac{1}{4}$
June	$2\frac{1}{4}$
July	$3\frac{7}{8}$
August	$3\frac{1}{4}$
September	$1\frac{5}{8}$
October	$3\frac{2}{8}$
November	$1\frac{3}{4}$
December	$1\frac{5}{8}$

2. What is the difference in rainfall from the wettest and driest months?

3. How much more rain fell in May than in April?

4. What is the combined rainfall amount for the summer months of June, July, and August?

5. How much more rain fell in the summer months than the combined rainfall for the last 4 months of the year?

6. In which months did it rain twice as much as it rained in December?

7. Each inch of rain can produce ten times that many inches of snow. If all of the rainfall in January was in the form of snow, how many inches of snow fell in January?

Name _____ Date _____

1. Find the sums.

a. $\frac{0}{3} + \frac{1}{3} + \frac{2}{3} + \frac{3}{3}$

b. $\frac{0}{4} + \frac{1}{4} + \frac{2}{4} + \frac{3}{4} + \frac{4}{4}$

c. $\frac{0}{5} + \frac{1}{5} + \frac{2}{5} + \frac{3}{5} + \frac{4}{5} + \frac{5}{5}$

d. $\frac{0}{6} + \frac{1}{6} + \frac{2}{6} + \frac{3}{6} + \frac{4}{6} + \frac{5}{6} + \frac{6}{6}$

e. $\frac{0}{7} + \frac{1}{7} + \frac{2}{7} + \frac{3}{7} + \frac{4}{7} + \frac{5}{7} + \frac{6}{7} + \frac{7}{7}$

f. $\frac{0}{8} + \frac{1}{8} + \frac{2}{8} + \frac{3}{8} + \frac{4}{8} + \frac{5}{8} + \frac{6}{8} + \frac{7}{8} + \frac{8}{8}$

2. Describe a pattern you notice when adding the sums of fractions with even denominators as opposed to those with odd denominators.

3. How would the sums change if the addition started with the unit fraction rather than with 0?

EUREKA
MATH™

Lesson 41: Find and use a pattern to calculate the sum of all fractional parts
between 0 and 1. Share and critique peer strategies.

169

4. Find the sums.

a. $\frac{0}{10} + \frac{1}{10} + \frac{2}{10} + \ldots \frac{10}{10}$

b. $\frac{0}{12} + \frac{1}{12} + \frac{2}{12} + \ldots \frac{12}{12}$

c. $\frac{0}{15} + \frac{1}{15} + \frac{2}{15} + \ldots + \frac{15}{15}$

d. $\frac{0}{25} + \frac{1}{25} + \frac{2}{25} + \ldots \frac{25}{25}$

e. $\frac{0}{50} + \frac{1}{50} + \frac{2}{50} + \ldots \frac{50}{50}$

f. $\frac{0}{100} + \frac{1}{100} + \frac{2}{100} + \ldots \frac{100}{100}$

5. Compare your strategy for finding the sums in Problems 4(d), 4(e), and 4(f) with a partner.

6. How can you apply this strategy to find the sum of all the whole numbers from 0 to 100?

Name _____   Date _____

. Find the sums.

a. $\frac{0}{5} + \frac{1}{5} + \frac{2}{5} + \frac{3}{5} + \frac{4}{5} + \frac{5}{5}$

b. $\frac{0}{6} + \frac{1}{6} + \frac{2}{6} + \frac{3}{6} + \frac{4}{6} + \frac{5}{6} + \frac{6}{6}$

c. $\frac{0}{7} + \frac{1}{7} + \frac{2}{7} + \frac{3}{7} + \frac{4}{7} + \frac{5}{7} + \frac{6}{7} + \frac{7}{7}$

d. $\frac{0}{8} + \frac{1}{8} + \frac{2}{8} + \frac{3}{8} + \frac{4}{8} + \frac{5}{8} + \frac{6}{8} + \frac{7}{8} + \frac{8}{8}$

e. $\frac{0}{9} + \frac{1}{9} + \frac{2}{9} + \frac{3}{9} + \frac{4}{9} + \frac{5}{9} + \frac{6}{9} + \frac{7}{9} + \frac{8}{9} + \frac{9}{9}$

f. $\frac{0}{10} + \frac{1}{10} + \frac{2}{10} + \frac{3}{10} + \frac{4}{10} + \frac{5}{10} + \frac{6}{10} + \frac{7}{10} + \frac{8}{10} + \frac{9}{10} + \frac{10}{10}$

. Describe a pattern you notice when adding the sums of fractions with even denominators as opposed to those with odd denominators.

3. How would the sums change if the addition started with the unit fraction rather than with 0?

EUREKA MATH™

Lesson 41:   Find and use a pattern to calculate the sum of all fractional parts between 0 and 1. Share and critique peer strategies.

171

4. Find the sums.

a. $\frac{0}{20} + \frac{1}{20} + \frac{2}{20} + \ldots \frac{20}{20}$

b. $\frac{0}{35} + \frac{1}{35} + \frac{2}{35} + \ldots \frac{35}{35}$

c. $\frac{0}{36} + \frac{1}{36} + \frac{2}{36} + \ldots + \frac{36}{36}$

d. $\frac{0}{75} + \frac{1}{75} + \frac{2}{75} + \ldots \frac{75}{75}$

e. $\frac{0}{100} + \frac{1}{100} + \frac{2}{100} + \ldots \frac{100}{100}$

f. $\frac{0}{99} + \frac{1}{99} + \frac{2}{99} + \ldots \frac{99}{99}$

5. How can you apply this strategy to find the sum of all the whole numbers from 0 to 50? To 99?

Lesson 41:   Find and use a pattern to calculate the sum of all fractional parts
between 0 and 1. Share and critique peer strategies.

Notes

Notes